MW00613547

Notary Journal Reorder Form

Yes! Please send me more of the Notary Public Journals!

Quantity: _____

Price: $11.99 plus $3.99 shipping per journal.

Save now! Order 2 journals and play only one shipping charge.

Please contact us at the numbers below for the current price and shipping cost. Ask about large quantity discounts.

Business Name: _____

Customer Name: _____

Address: _____ Suite/Floor _____

Address Line 2: _____

City _____ State _____ Zip _____

Phone (Day): _____ Phone (Eve.): _____

E-mail: _____ Commission Expiration Date:_____

Please bill my credit card: Type: ☐   ☐   ☐   ☐

Number: _____ Expiration Date: _____

Cardholder Signature: _____

Customers will be contacted with the final invoice total.

4 easy ways to reorder:

☎ CALL: Toll Free 866-986-7446

 INTERNET: www.notarytainer.com

Complete the order form in this journal and send along with payment via the following methods:

🖨 FAX: 732-553-0330 • 24-Hour Confidential Fax

📪 MAIL: Notary Trainer, 303 South Feltus Street, South Amboy, NJ 08879

For a complete list of available notary supplies, visit www.NotaryTrainer.com.

ver 8/06

cut on the dotted line

To better prepare you for your responsibilities as a Notary Public, visit www.NotaryTrainer.com for online notary education.

<u>Online courses include:</u>

- ▶ Prepare for the New York Notary Exam
- ▶ Practice and Pass the New York Notary Exam
- ▶ Notary Basics
- ▶ Advanced Notary Topics
- ▶ Notary Signing Agent - Introduction
- ▶ Notary Signing Agent - Intermediate
- ▶ Notary Signing Agent - Advanced
- ▶ Earn Money as a Notary Public

Personal Appearance: Appearing face to face and in the same room with a notary at the time of notarization.

Personal Knowledge: Familiarity with an individual resulting from interactions over a period of time sufficient to eliminate every reasonable doubt that the individual has the identity claimed.

Plaintiff: The party that initiates a civil suit.

Positive Identification: Knowing who a person is without reasonable doubt or suspicion.

Power of Attorney: A legal document that authorizes another person to act on one's behalf.

Public Record: Any record open to the public for inspection.

Real Estate Settlement Procedures Act (RESPA): A consumer protection law that requires lenders to give borrowers advance notice of closing costs.

Reasonable Care: The degree of care that a person of reasonable judgment would take under like circumstances.

Reconveyance: The act of returning title to a trustor when the Note secured by a Deed of Trust is satisfied.

Recording: The noting in the registrar's office of the details of a properly executed Deed, Mortgage Note, or other legal instrument, making the instrument a part of the public record.

Refinancing: The process of paying off one loan with the proceeds from a new loan, using the same property as security.

Representative Capacity: Status of signing or acting on behalf of another person or on behalf of a legal entity, such as a corporation, partnership, or trust.

Right to Cancel; Right of Rescission: An option on refinance and other loans creating a lien on property that gives a borrower three (3) business days to cancel the loan.

Satisfactory Evidence: Amount of proof that satisfies credibility beyond a reasonable doubt.

Second Mortgage: A mortgage that has a lien position subordinate to the first mortgage.

Security: The property that will be pledged as collateral for a loan.

Security Instrument: An instrument used to identify and encumber real property used as collateral for a loan. Instrument is notarized and then recorded in the county where property is located. Once recorded, it secures an interest in, or lien against, the property. The security instrument used is state specific. Examples are deed of trust, security deed, a trust deed, or a mortgage.

Subscribing Witness: One who witnesses a signing of an instrument and testifies to that fact.

Title: Written evidence of the right of ownership in property.

Title Search: An examination of city, town, or county records to determine the legal ownership of real estate and the outstanding liens and claims against the real estate.

Trustee: A fiduciary that holds or controls property for the benefit of another.

Truth in Lending Act (TILA): A federal law that promotes the informed use of consumer credit by requiring disclosures about its terms and costs.

Unauthorized or Unlawful Practice of Law (UPL): Practice of law by a person who is not a legal professional, typically defined as helping another person to draft, prepare, complete, select, or understand a document or transaction.

Venue: The location (state and county) where the notary and signer are standing at the time the notarial act takes place.

Witness: One who observes an act as it happens. A witness may be requested to testify about the act witnessed.

Some key issues are covered in the following pages to serve as a reference for proper notarial procedures. Included are steps to follow, issues to avoid, sample forms, and general information of importance to the notary public. If you have questions or would like to order supplies, please contact us at the addresses and phone numbers listed within this publication.

VERBAL CEREMONIES

Notaries often overlook one of the most important elements of a proper notarization - the verbal ceremony. Signers must be placed under oath; that is, the notary must 'administer' an oath or affirmation, if one is required, and if an acknowledgment is necessary, the notary must 'take' the verbal, spoken acknowledgment of the signer or signers before them.

An affirmation is the legal equivalent of an oath and may be used in place of an oath for a signer who may have religious or other reasons for refusing to swear to an oath. An affirmation is just as binding as the oath under law.

The following wording will properly fulfill the notary's responsibility for the verbal ceremonies:

OATH/AFFIRMATION

For an Individual

Oath

"Do you solemnly swear under penalties of perjury that the information contained in this document is the truth, so help you God?"

Affirmation

"Do you affirm under penalties of perjury that the statements included in this document are true and correct to the best of your belief?"

For a Corporation or Partnership Representative

Oath

"Do you solemnly swear under penalties of perjury that you have personal knowledge of the facts to be sworn, that the information contained in this document is the truth, and that you have the authority to sign for the corporation/ partnership, so help you God?"

Affirmation

"Do you solemnly affirm under penalties of perjury that you have personal knowledge of the facts to be affirmed, that the information contained in this document is the truth, and that you have the authority to sign for the corporation/partnership?"

ACKNOWLEDGMENT

For an Individual

"Do you acknowledge and declare that this is your signature, that you understand this document, and that you willingly signed this document for the purposes stated herein?"

For a Corporation or Partnership

"Do you acknowledge and declare that this is your signature, that you understand this document, that you have the authority to sign for the corporation/partnership, and that you willingly signed this document for the purposes stated herein?"

For all of the above, the signer should answer 'yes' or 'I do.'

Every notary should follow a consistent checklist with each notarial act performed, to ensure that no important step is overlooked. An error may be costly, and with a little caution, most can be avoided. Notaries should adhere closely to the following checklist in order to minimize opportunities for fraud and error.

NOTARY CHECKLIST

✓ Insist on the personal appearance of every signer when any notarial act takes place, regardless of the type of act required. Never perform any notarial act if the signer is not standing before you at the time of notarization.

✓ Review the notarial certificate to determine which notarial act is required.

✓ Review the document to ensure that it is complete, with no blank spaces and no correction fluid, and is dated no later than the date of the notarial act. (It is acceptable if the document was created before the notarization date.)

✓ Clearly establish the identity of the signer(s) named in the document and any witnesses present.

✓ Complete the journal entry, including names, signatures, and addresses of all signers and witnesses.

✓ Notarize signatures for only those signers appearing before you. If other signatures are required, clearly detail which signers actually appeared before you (list each by name on the notarial certificate) so that it is apparent exactly whose signatures you are notarizing and whose you are not.

✓ Perform the verbal ceremony. That is, administer an oath/affirmation or take the spoken acknowledgment of those signing the document as appropriate, before you complete, sign, and impress your notary stamp or embosser on the notarial certificate.

✓ Observe the signing of each original signature on any document requiring the administration of an oath or affirmation.

The notary should always:

✓ Act as an impartial witness with no personal gain or involvement in the transaction taking place. If you or someone close to you stands to gain in any way, refer the signer to another notary to ensure impartiality.

✓ Maintain complete confidentiality regarding all notarial acts signed in your presence. High ethics are the foundation of a proper notarization.

WHEN TO SAY NO

The Notary must refuse to notarize if:
- The signer is not in the notary's presence at the time the notary act is completed.
- The signer is unknown to the notary and cannot provide proper identification documents.
- The document is dated for a later date than the date of notarization.
- The document has blank spaces that the signer is unable to complete before the notarization.
- The notary is involved personally in the transaction to be notarized.
- The signer refuses to take an oath or affirmation, or will not acknowledge a signature on a document.
- The notary has reliable reason to believe the signer cannot comprehend the action taking place.
- The signer appears confused or is under the influence of alcohol or medication.
- The signer appears to be coerced into signing against his/her will.
- The notary has reliable reason to believe the transaction is fraudulent or unlawful.
- The documents are in a language the notary or the signer cannot understand.

Require Personal Appearance and Proof of Identity for Every Notarization

A notary's first responsibility is to require the personal appearance of the signer. It is unlawful to notarize a signature without the appearance of the signer, under any circumstances. If the document is signed and requires an acknowledgment, the notary must have the signer in his or her presence to take the signer's verbal acknowledgment of that signature as his/her own and willfully made. If the document requires an oath or affirmation, the notary must have the signer in his or her presence to administer the oath, and must also witness the actual signing of the document as required by law.

Evidence of Identity: If the notary personally knows the signer, then he/she may check the box 'personally known' in the space provided in the notarial journal. However, unless the notary knows the individual well enough to state so under oath if ever called to testify in court, the notary must take reasonable care to properly identify the signer.

The best identification is a government-issued identification card such as a driver's license or state identification card that contains a signature, photograph, physical description, and an ID number.

The following forms of identification are recommended:
- ✓ Photo Driver's License or state-issued ID card (state laws vary on expiration)
- ✓ United States or Foreign Passport
- ✓ Alien Registration Card (Green Card)
- ✓ US Military ID Card
- ✓ US Naturalization Certificate

Credible Witness - Where Allowed by Law

Notaries in some states may also rely on a credible witness for the identification of a signer if the signer is not personally known to the notary. A credible witness is an impartial person unaffected by the document or transaction who is personally known to the notary and who personally knows the individual appearing before a notary and takes an oath or affirmation to vouch for that individual's identity. Some states require two witnesses if unknown to the notary. Other states do not accept this form of identification of a signer. Know your state's laws regarding acceptable forms of identification that a notary may use.

JOURNAL OF NOTARIAL ACTS

A journal of notarial acts is a detailed, chronological, permanently bound record of the official acts of a notary. Every notarization should be documented in the journal, which is required by law in many states.

Each notarization and signer should have a separate journal entry. The notary journal should be a securely bound book with consecutively numbered pages and entries to deter unauthorized insertions and deletions. The journal should be kept for seven years after the expiration, resignation, or revocation of the notary's commission.

The journal can protect notaries as well as signers by providing valuable evidence if a notarized document is lost or altered after the notarization, or if any facts about the transaction are later challenged in a court of law. Also, the journal can protect the notary from baseless but damaging allegations of wrongdoing by showing that reasonable care was exercised in identifying signers and performing notarial acts.

Completing the Entry in the Journal of Notarial Acts

This notary journal is designed for ease of use and simplicity in format. Blanks are to be completed as needed. Be sure to complete your journal entry <u>before</u> you perform the notarization so the signer doesn't simply take the completed document and leave before you can complete your journal entry.

Printed Name of Signer: John Q. Adams	Signer's Signature: John Q. Adams	Time AM/PM: 10 a.m. Date Notarized: 12/21/2006	**2**

Signer's Complete Address: 1234 Park Avenue	City: Boston	State: MA	Zip: 02134	Phone: 617 555· 1212

Identification by: ☑ Identification Card   Issued By: Mass DMV   I.D. # 512345678

☐ Personal Knowledge   ☐ Credible Witness(es)   Type of I.D.: driver lic.   Expiration Date: 12/3/2011   Date of Birth: 12·3·73

Type of Notarial Act: ☐ Verbal Ceremony Performed   ☐ Other (Describe):   Fee: $
☑ Oath/Affirmation   ☐ Acknowledgment   Travel: $

Right Thumbprint of Signer

Type of Document: Affidavit   Date of Document: 12/20/06   Witness(es) Present ☐ Yes ☑ No   Other Signer(s) Present ☐ Yes ☑ No

Witness: Printed Name: N/A   Address/Phone   Signature of Witness

Comments; Additional Information: Signer verbally swore to oath

If Notarization Failed or Refused, Give Reason: ☐ Insufficient ID   ☐ Signer Confused   ☐ Other (Explain in Comments Field)

Safeguarding the Journal

The journal of notarial acts should be kept in a secure place, under the notary's exclusive control, preferably in a locked and fireproof drawer, file, or safe. **<u>Never share your journal or your notary equipment with anyone.</u>** You must safeguard your journal and all other notarial records and surrender or destroy them only by rule of law, by court order, or at the direction of the notary administrator's office for your state.

Thumbprints in the Journal

Due to the increase of fraud and identity theft, more notaries are adopting the practice of requesting signers to affix a thumbprint in the official journal as a measure to deter fraud. This action deters impostors who will not want to leave behind such absolute evidence of an attempted fraud, and provides proof that the signer actually appeared before a notary if this fact is later challenged. Though in most states notaries are not required to obtain a fingerprint or thumbprint from signers, this is a highly effective means of fraud prevention. Honest and reputable signers will often appreciate the extra element of security you provide by requesting a thumbprint for their own protection, and are happy to comply.

The notary must not refuse to notarize if a signer refuses to provide a thumbprint, unless this is required by law as a condition of notarization in your state.

Sample Notarial Certificates

In notarizing any document, the notary must complete, sign, and affix the official notary stamp or embossing seal to the notarial wording certificate, which is the notary's official testimony providing true and exact details about the notarization. Enter the ID number in the journal, but not on the certificate, for the identity security of your signer. On the certificate, show how identified, i.e. '(State) Driver's License' or 'personally known' if a space is provided.

Venue

State of _____
County of _____

The term 'venue' describes the actual location, county and state, where the signers and the notary are standing at the time of notarization. Notaries often complete the venue incorrectly, entering the county of residence or employment, or where the commission was issued.

The venue must be completed on every notarial certificate, and must accurately describe the state/commonwealth and county where the signer(s) and the notary are standing at the time the notarial act takes place. If the wrong information is entered when presented to the notary, the incorrect information should be lined through and initialed, and the correct information should be entered.

Sample Jurat Certificate Wording for Oath/Affirmation

State of _____
County of _____

Subscribed and sworn to (or affirmed) before me this _____ day of _____, 20____, by (name of person making statement).

____Personally Known   ____Produced Identification

Type of ID Produced _____

_____
(Signature of Notary)

NOTARY STAMP
OR SEAL

_____
(Name of Notary Typed, Stamped, or Printed)

Notary Public, State of _____

Sample Acknowledgment Certificate

State of _____
County of _____

The foregoing instrument was acknowledged before me on this ____day of _____, 20___ by (name of person acknowledging signature), who acknowledged to me that he/she willingly signed and executed the instrument for the purposes stated in it.

____Personally Known   ____Produced Identification

Type of ID Produced _____

Given under my hand and seal of office this ____ day of _____, 20____.

_____
(Signature of Notary)

NOTARY STAMP
OR SEAL

_____
(Name of Notary Typed, Stamped, or Printed)

Notary Public, State of _____

Get your notary supply package fast.

Most order arrive in just 3 business days or less to the NE states!

You get a Notary Embosser, Self-inking Rubber Stamp and a Notary Journal

Complete this fax order form and we will do the rest!

Jane C. Notary
Any State Usa
Commission ID: 987654
My Comm. Exp.: 12/31/2012

NotaryTrainer.com Supply Order Form - Confidential Fax: 732-553–0330

Please Check one box: Ship to my: ☐ Business Address   ☐ Residential Address

Print Clearly

Name as Commissioned: _____
          First Name   Middle   Last Name

Company/Business Name: _____

Shipping Address: _____ St/ FLR/ Department: _____

City: _____ State: _____ Zip: _____

Day Phone: (_____) _____ Fax : (_____) _____

E-mail for confirmation only: _____

Notary Commission ID Number: _____

Qualification County/City: _____ Residence County/City: _____

Notary Commission Expiration Date: _____ ☐ Leave off Notary Commission Date

Visit www.NotaryTrainer.com for more quality notary supplies

Email: sales@notarytrainer.com

Fax: 732-553-0330 • 24-Hour Confidential Fax

Phone: 1-866-986-7446

Make checks payable to: NotaryTrainer.com 303 South Feltus St., South Amboy, NJ 08879

Please bill my credit card: ☐ AMERICAN EXPRESS   ☐ DISCOVER   ☐ MasterCard   ☐ VISA

Card number _____ Name on card_____

Expiration date_____ Validation Code (BACK/ FRONT OF CARD) _____

Subtotal	$55.00	
Shipping	7.95	*UPS or USPS*
Tax	$_____	*NJ Residents, please add sales tax*
Total	$_____	

NotaryTrainer.com offers Notary Public Supplies made specifically for your state.

7

Printed Name of Signer:	Signer's Signature:	Time AM/PM: _____
CHRY		Date Notarized: _____

Signer's Complete Address:	City	State	Zip	Phone

Identification by: ❏ Identification Card   Issued By: _____   I.D. # _____

❏ Personal Knowledge   ❏ Credible Witness(es)   Type of I.D.: _____   Expiration Date: _____   Date of Birth: _____

Type of Notarial Act: ❏ Verbal Ceremony Performed   ❏ Other (Describe): _____   Fee: $ _____   Travel: $ _____

❏ Oath/Affirmation   ❏ Acknowledgment

Type of Document   Date of Document   Witness(es) Present ❏ Yes ❏ No   Other Signer(s) Present ❏ Yes ❏ No

Right Thumbprint of Signer

Witness: Printed Name   Address/Phone   Signature of Witness

Comments; Additional Information: If Notarization Failed or Refused, Give Reason:

❏ Insufficient ID   ❏ Signer Confused   ❏ Other (Explain in Comments Field)

8

Printed Name of Signer:	Signer's Signature:	Time AM/PM: _____
Ger		Date Notarized: _____

Signer's Complete Address:	City	State	Zip	Phone

Identification by: ❏ Identification Card   Issued By: _____   I.D. # _____

❏ Personal Knowledge   ❏ Credible Witness(es)   Type of I.D.: _____   Expiration Date: _____   Date of Birth: _____

Type of Notarial Act: ❏ Verbal Ceremony Performed   ❏ Other (Describe): _____   Fee: $ _____   Travel: $ _____

❏ Oath/Affirmation   ❏ Acknowledgment

Type of Document   Date of Document   Witness(es) Present ❏ Yes ❏ No   Other Signer(s) Present ❏ Yes ❏ No

Right Thumbprint of Signer

Witness: Printed Name   Address/Phone   Signature of Witness

Comments; Additional Information: If Notarization Failed or Refused, Give Reason:

❏ Insufficient ID   ❏ Signer Confused   ❏ Other (Explain in Comments Field)

9

Printed Name of Signer:	Signer's Signature:	Time AM/PM: _____
		Date Notarized: _____

Signer's Complete Address:	City	State	Zip	Phone

Identification by: ❏ Identification Card   Issued By: _____   I.D. # _____

❏ Personal Knowledge   ❏ Credible Witness(es)   Type of I.D.: _____   Expiration Date: _____   Date of Birth: _____

Type of Notarial Act: ❏ Verbal Ceremony Performed   ❏ Other (Describe): _____   Fee: $ _____   Travel: $ _____

❏ Oath/Affirmation   ❏ Acknowledgment

Type of Document   Date of Document   Witness(es) Present ❏ Yes ❏ No   Other Signer(s) Present ❏ Yes ❏ No

Right Thumbprint of Signer

Witness: Printed Name   Address/Phone   Signature of Witness

Comments; Additional Information: If Notarization Failed or Refused, Give Reason:

❏ Insufficient ID   ❏ Signer Confused   ❏ Other (Explain in Comments Field)

10

| Printed Name of Signer: | Signer's Signature: | Time AM/PM: _____ |
| | | Date Notarized: _____ |

| Signer's Complete Address: | City | State | Zip | Phone |

Identification by: ❑ Identification Card   Issued By: _____   I.D. # _____

❑ Personal Knowledge   ❑ Credible Witness(es)   Type of I.D.: _____   Expiration Date: _____   Date of Birth: _____

Type of Notarial Act: ❑ Verbal Ceremony Performed   ❑ Other (Describe):   Fee: $

❑ Oath/Affirmation   ❑ Acknowledgment   Travel: $

| Type of Document | Date of Document | Witness(es) Present | Other Signer(s) Present | Right Thumbprint of Signer |
| | | ❑ Yes ❑ No | ❑ Yes ❑ No | |

Witness: Printed Name   Address/Phone   Signature of Witness

Comments; Additional Information:

If Notarization Failed or Refused, Give Reason:

❑ Insufficient ID   ❑ Signer Confused   ❑ Other (Explain in Comments Field)

11

| Printed Name of Signer: | Signer's Signature: | Time AM/PM: _____ |
| | | Date Notarized: _____ |

| Signer's Complete Address: | City | State | Zip | Phone |

Identification by: ❑ Identification Card   Issued By: _____   I.D. # _____

❑ Personal Knowledge   ❑ Credible Witness(es)   Type of I.D.: _____   Expiration Date: _____   Date of Birth: _____

Type of Notarial Act: ❑ Verbal Ceremony Performed   ❑ Other (Describe):   Fee: $

❑ Oath/Affirmation   ❑ Acknowledgment   Travel: $

| Type of Document | Date of Document | Witness(es) Present | Other Signer(s) Present | Right Thumbprint of Signer |
| | | ❑ Yes ❑ No | ❑ Yes ❑ No | |

Witness: Printed Name   Address/Phone   Signature of Witness

Comments; Additional Information:

If Notarization Failed or Refused, Give Reason:

❑ Insufficient ID   ❑ Signer Confused   ❑ Other (Explain in Comments Field)

12

| Printed Name of Signer: | Signer's Signature: | Time AM/PM: _____ |
| | | Date Notarized: _____ |

| Signer's Complete Address: | City | State | Zip | Phone |

Identification by: ❑ Identification Card   Issued By: _____   I.D. # _____

❑ Personal Knowledge   ❑ Credible Witness(es)   Type of I.D.: _____   Expiration Date: _____   Date of Birth: _____

Type of Notarial Act: ❑ Verbal Ceremony Performed   ❑ Other (Describe):   Fee: $

❑ Oath/Affirmation   ❑ Acknowledgment   Travel: $

| Type of Document | Date of Document | Witness(es) Present | Other Signer(s) Present | Right Thumbprint of Signer |
| | | ❑ Yes ❑ No | ❑ Yes ❑ No | |

Witness: Printed Name   Address/Phone   Signature of Witness

Comments; Additional Information:

If Notarization Failed or Refused, Give Reason:

❑ Insufficient ID   ❑ Signer Confused   ❑ Other (Explain in Comments Field)

13

| Printed Name of Signer: | Signer's Signature: | Time AM/PM: _____ |
| | | Date Notarized: _____ |

Signer's Complete Address: City   State   Zip   Phone

Identification by: ❏ Identification Card   Issued By: _____   I.D. # _____

❏ Personal Knowledge   ❏ Credible Witness(es)   Type of I.D.: _____   Expiration Date: _____   Date of Birth: _____

Type of Notarial Act: ❏ Verbal Ceremony Performed   ❏ Other (Describe): _____   Fee: $ _____

❏ Oath/Affirmation   ❏ Acknowledgment   Travel: $ _____

Type of Document   Date of Document   Witness(es) Present   Other Signer(s) Present   *Right Thumbprint of Signer*

     ❏ Yes ❏ No   ❏ Yes ❏ No

Witness: Printed Name   Address/Phone   Signature of Witness

Comments; Additional Information: If Notarization Failed or Refused, Give Reason:

     ❏ Insufficient ID   ❏ Signer Confused   ❏ Other (Explain in Comments Field)

14

| Printed Name of Signer: | Signer's Signature: | Time AM/PM: _____ |
| | | Date Notarized: _____ |

Signer's Complete Address: City   State   Zip   Phone

Identification by: ❏ Identification Card   Issued By: _____   I.D. # _____

❏ Personal Knowledge   ❏ Credible Witness(es)   Type of I.D.: _____   Expiration Date: _____   Date of Birth: _____

Type of Notarial Act: ❏ Verbal Ceremony Performed   ❏ Other (Describe): _____   Fee: $ _____

❏ Oath/Affirmation   ❏ Acknowledgment   Travel: $ _____

Type of Document   Date of Document   Witness(es) Present   Other Signer(s) Present   *Right Thumbprint of Signer*

     ❏ Yes ❏ No   ❏ Yes ❏ No

Witness: Printed Name   Address/Phone   Signature of Witness

Comments; Additional Information: If Notarization Failed or Refused, Give Reason:

     ❏ Insufficient ID   ❏ Signer Confused   ❏ Other (Explain in Comments Field)

15

| Printed Name of Signer: | Signer's Signature: | Time AM/PM: _____ |
| | | Date Notarized: _____ |

Signer's Complete Address: City   State   Zip   Phone

Identification by: ❏ Identification Card   Issued By: _____   I.D. # _____

❏ Personal Knowledge   ❏ Credible Witness(es)   Type of I.D.: _____   Expiration Date: _____   Date of Birth: _____

Type of Notarial Act: ❏ Verbal Ceremony Performed   ❏ Other (Describe): _____   Fee: $ _____

❏ Oath/Affirmation   ❏ Acknowledgment   Travel: $ _____

Type of Document   Date of Document   Witness(es) Present   Other Signer(s) Present   *Right Thumbprint of Signer*

     ❏ Yes ❏ No   ❏ Yes ❏ No

Witness: Printed Name   Address/Phone   Signature of Witness

Comments; Additional Information: If Notarization Failed or Refused, Give Reason:

     ❏ Insufficient ID   ❏ Signer Confused   ❏ Other (Explain in Comments Field)

16

| Printed Name of Signer: | Signer's Signature: | Time AM/PM: _____ |
| | | Date Notarized: _____ |

Signer's Complete Address: City   State   Zip   Phone

Identification by: ❑ Identification Card   Issued By: _____   I.D. # _____

❑ Personal Knowledge   ❑ Credible Witness(es)   Type of I.D.: _____   Expiration Date: _____   Date of Birth: _____

Type of Notarial Act: ❑ Verbal Ceremony Performed   ❑ Other (Describe):   Fee: $

❑ Oath/Affirmation   ❑ Acknowledgment   Travel: $

Type of Document   Date of Document   Witness(es) Present   Other Signer(s) Present
          ❑ Yes ❑ No   ❑ Yes ❑ No

Witness: Printed Name   Address/Phone   Signature of Witness

Right Thumbprint of Signer

Comments; Additional Information: If Notarization Failed or Refused, Give Reason:

❑ Insufficient ID   ❑ Signer Confused   ❑ Other (Explain in Comments Field)

17

| Printed Name of Signer: | Signer's Signature: | Time AM/PM: _____ |
| | | Date Notarized: _____ |

Signer's Complete Address: City   State   Zip   Phone

Identification by: ❑ Identification Card   Issued By: _____   I.D. # _____

❑ Personal Knowledge   ❑ Credible Witness(es)   Type of I.D.: _____   Expiration Date: _____   Date of Birth: _____

Type of Notarial Act: ❑ Verbal Ceremony Performed   ❑ Other (Describe):   Fee: $

❑ Oath/Affirmation   ❑ Acknowledgment   Travel: $

Type of Document   Date of Document   Witness(es) Present   Other Signer(s) Present
          ❑ Yes ❑ No   ❑ Yes ❑ No

Witness: Printed Name   Address/Phone   Signature of Witness

Right Thumbprint of Signer

Comments; Additional Information: If Notarization Failed or Refused, Give Reason:

❑ Insufficient ID   ❑ Signer Confused   ❑ Other (Explain in Comments Field)

18

| Printed Name of Signer: | Signer's Signature: | Time AM/PM: _____ |
| | | Date Notarized: _____ |

Signer's Complete Address: City   State   Zip   Phone

Identification by: ❑ Identification Card   Issued By: _____   I.D. # _____

❑ Personal Knowledge   ❑ Credible Witness(es)   Type of I.D.: _____   Expiration Date: _____   Date of Birth: _____

Type of Notarial Act: ❑ Verbal Ceremony Performed   ❑ Other (Describe):   Fee: $

❑ Oath/Affirmation   ❑ Acknowledgment   Travel: $

Type of Document   Date of Document   Witness(es) Present   Other Signer(s) Present
          ❑ Yes ❑ No   ❑ Yes ❑ No

Witness: Printed Name   Address/Phone   Signature of Witness

Right Thumbprint of Signer

Comments; Additional Information: If Notarization Failed or Refused, Give Reason:

❑ Insufficient ID   ❑ Signer Confused   ❑ Other (Explain in Comments Field)

19

Printed Name of Signer:

Signer's Signature:

Time AM/PM: _____

Date Notarized: _____

Signer's Complete Address:　　City　　　　　　　State　　Zip　　　　Phone

Identification by:　　❑ Identification Card　　Issued By: _____　I.D. # _____

❑ Personal Knowledge　　❑ Credible Witness(es)　　Type of I.D.: _____　Expiration Date: _____　Date of Birth: _____

Type of Notarial Act:　　❑ Verbal Ceremony Performed　　❑ Other (Describe): 　　　　　　Fee: $

❑ Oath/Affirmation　　❑ Acknowledgment　　　　　　　　　　　　　　Travel: $

Type of Document　　　　Date of Document　　Witness(es) Present　　Other Signer(s) Present

　　　　　　　　　　　　　　　　　❑ Yes ❑ No　　　❑ Yes ❑ No

Right Thumbprint of Signer

Witness: Printed Name　　　Address/Phone　　　　Signature of Witness

Comments; Additional Information:　　　　　　If Notarization Failed or Refused, Give Reason:

❑ Insufficient ID　　❑ Signer Confused　　❑ Other (Explain in Comments Field)

20

Printed Name of Signer:

Signer's Signature:

Time AM/PM: _____

Date Notarized: _____

Signer's Complete Address:　　City　　　　　　　State　　Zip　　　　Phone

Identification by:　　❑ Identification Card　　Issued By: _____　I.D. # _____

❑ Personal Knowledge　　❑ Credible Witness(es)　　Type of I.D.: _____　Expiration Date: _____　Date of Birth: _____

Type of Notarial Act:　　❑ Verbal Ceremony Performed　　❑ Other (Describe): 　　　　　　Fee: $

❑ Oath/Affirmation　　❑ Acknowledgment　　　　　　　　　　　　　　Travel: $

Type of Document　　　　Date of Document　　Witness(es) Present　　Other Signer(s) Present

　　　　　　　　　　　　　　　　　❑ Yes ❑ No　　　❑ Yes ❑ No

Right Thumbprint of Signer

Witness: Printed Name　　　Address/Phone　　　　Signature of Witness

Comments; Additional Information:　　　　　　If Notarization Failed or Refused, Give Reason:

❑ Insufficient ID　　❑ Signer Confused　　❑ Other (Explain in Comments Field)

21

Printed Name of Signer:

Signer's Signature:

Time AM/PM: _____

Date Notarized: _____

Signer's Complete Address:　　City　　　　　　　State　　Zip　　　　Phone

Identification by:　　❑ Identification Card　　Issued By: _____　I.D. # _____

❑ Personal Knowledge　　❑ Credible Witness(es)　　Type of I.D.: _____　Expiration Date: _____　Date of Birth: _____

Type of Notarial Act:　　❑ Verbal Ceremony Performed　　❑ Other (Describe): 　　　　　　Fee: $

❑ Oath/Affirmation　　❑ Acknowledgment　　　　　　　　　　　　　　Travel: $

Type of Document　　　　Date of Document　　Witness(es) Present　　Other Signer(s) Present

　　　　　　　　　　　　　　　　　❑ Yes ❑ No　　　❑ Yes ❑ No

Right Thumbprint of Signer

Witness: Printed Name　　　Address/Phone　　　　Signature of Witness

Comments; Additional Information:　　　　　　If Notarization Failed or Refused, Give Reason:

❑ Insufficient ID　　❑ Signer Confused　　❑ Other (Explain in Comments Field)

22

| Printed Name of Signer: | Signer's Signature: | Time AM/PM: _____ |
| | | Date Notarized: _____ |

| Signer's Complete Address: | City | State | Zip | Phone |

| Identification by: | ❑ Identification Card | Issued By: _____ | I.D. # _____ |
| ❑ Personal Knowledge | ❑ Credible Witness(es) | Type of I.D.: _____ | Expiration Date: _____ | Date of Birth: _____ |

| Type of Notarial Act: | ❑ Verbal Ceremony Performed | ❑ Other (Describe): | Fee: $ | |
| ❑ Oath/Affirmation | ❑ Acknowledgment | | Travel: $ | |

| Type of Document | Date of Document | Witness(es) Present | Other Signer(s) Present | Right Thumbprint of Signer |
| | | ❑ Yes ❑ No | ❑ Yes ❑ No | |

| Witness: Printed Name | Address/Phone | Signature of Witness | |

| Comments; Additional Information: | If Notarization Failed or Refused, Give Reason: |
| | ❑ Insufficient ID ❑ Signer Confused ❑ Other (Explain in Comments Field) |

23

| Printed Name of Signer: | Signer's Signature: | Time AM/PM: _____ |
| | | Date Notarized: _____ |

| Signer's Complete Address: | City | State | Zip | Phone |

| Identification by: | ❑ Identification Card | Issued By: _____ | I.D. # _____ |
| ❑ Personal Knowledge | ❑ Credible Witness(es) | Type of I.D.: _____ | Expiration Date: _____ | Date of Birth: _____ |

| Type of Notarial Act: | ❑ Verbal Ceremony Performed | ❑ Other (Describe): | Fee: $ | |
| ❑ Oath/Affirmation | ❑ Acknowledgment | | Travel: $ | |

| Type of Document | Date of Document | Witness(es) Present | Other Signer(s) Present | Right Thumbprint of Signer |
| | | ❑ Yes ❑ No | ❑ Yes ❑ No | |

| Witness: Printed Name | Address/Phone | Signature of Witness | |

| Comments; Additional Information: | If Notarization Failed or Refused, Give Reason: |
| | ❑ Insufficient ID ❑ Signer Confused ❑ Other (Explain in Comments Field) |

24

| Printed Name of Signer: | Signer's Signature: | Time AM/PM: _____ |
| | | Date Notarized: _____ |

| Signer's Complete Address: | City | State | Zip | Phone |

| Identification by: | ❑ Identification Card | Issued By: _____ | I.D. # _____ |
| ❑ Personal Knowledge | ❑ Credible Witness(es) | Type of I.D.: _____ | Expiration Date: _____ | Date of Birth: _____ |

| Type of Notarial Act: | ❑ Verbal Ceremony Performed | ❑ Other (Describe): | Fee: $ | |
| ❑ Oath/Affirmation | ❑ Acknowledgment | | Travel: $ | |

| Type of Document | Date of Document | Witness(es) Present | Other Signer(s) Present | Right Thumbprint of Signer |
| | | ❑ Yes ❑ No | ❑ Yes ❑ No | |

| Witness: Printed Name | Address/Phone | Signature of Witness | |

| Comments; Additional Information: | If Notarization Failed or Refused, Give Reason: |
| | ❑ Insufficient ID ❑ Signer Confused ❑ Other (Explain in Comments Field) |

25

| Printed Name of Signer: | Signer's Signature: | Time AM/PM: _____ |
| | | Date Notarized: _____ |

Signer's Complete Address: City   State   Zip   Phone

Identification by: ❏ Identification Card   Issued By: _____   I.D. # _____

❏ Personal Knowledge   ❏ Credible Witness(es)   Type of I.D.: _____   Expiration Date: _____   Date of Birth: _____

Type of Notarial Act: ❏ Verbal Ceremony Performed   ❏ Other (Describe):   Fee: $ Right Thumbprint of Signer
❏ Oath/Affirmation   ❏ Acknowledgment   Travel: $

Type of Document   Date of Document   Witness(es) Present   Other Signer(s) Present
                                        ❏ Yes ❏ No   ❏ Yes ❏ No

Witness: Printed Name   Address/Phone   Signature of Witness

Comments; Additional Information: If Notarization Failed or Refused, Give Reason:
    ❏ Insufficient ID   ❏ Signer Confused   ❏ Other (Explain in Comments Field)

26

| Printed Name of Signer: | Signer's Signature: | Time AM/PM: _____ |
| | | Date Notarized: _____ |

Signer's Complete Address: City   State   Zip   Phone

Identification by: ❏ Identification Card   Issued By: _____   I.D. # _____

❏ Personal Knowledge   ❏ Credible Witness(es)   Type of I.D.: _____   Expiration Date: _____   Date of Birth: _____

Type of Notarial Act: ❏ Verbal Ceremony Performed   ❏ Other (Describe):   Fee: $ Right Thumbprint of Signer
❏ Oath/Affirmation   ❏ Acknowledgment   Travel: $

Type of Document   Date of Document   Witness(es) Present   Other Signer(s) Present
                                        ❏ Yes ❏ No   ❏ Yes ❏ No

Witness: Printed Name   Address/Phone   Signature of Witness

Comments; Additional Information: If Notarization Failed or Refused, Give Reason:
    ❏ Insufficient ID   ❏ Signer Confused   ❏ Other (Explain in Comments Field)

27

| Printed Name of Signer: | Signer's Signature: | Time AM/PM: _____ |
| | | Date Notarized: _____ |

Signer's Complete Address: City   State   Zip   Phone

Identification by: ❏ Identification Card   Issued By: _____   I.D. # _____

❏ Personal Knowledge   ❏ Credible Witness(es)   Type of I.D.: _____   Expiration Date: _____   Date of Birth: _____

Type of Notarial Act: ❏ Verbal Ceremony Performed   ❏ Other (Describe):   Fee: $ Right Thumbprint of Signer
❏ Oath/Affirmation   ❏ Acknowledgment   Travel: $

Type of Document   Date of Document   Witness(es) Present   Other Signer(s) Present
                                        ❏ Yes ❏ No   ❏ Yes ❏ No

Witness: Printed Name   Address/Phone   Signature of Witness

Comments; Additional Information: If Notarization Failed or Refused, Give Reason:
    ❏ Insufficient ID   ❏ Signer Confused   ❏ Other (Explain in Comments Field)

28

| Printed Name of Signer: | Signer's Signature: | Time AM/PM: _____ |
| | | Date Notarized: _____ |

| Signer's Complete Address: | City | State | Zip | Phone |
| | | | | |

Identification by: ❑ Identification Card   Issued By: _____ I.D. # _____

❑ Personal Knowledge ❑ Credible Witness(es) Type of I.D.: _____ Expiration Date: _____ Date of Birth: _____

| Type of Notarial Act: | ❑ Verbal Ceremony Performed | ❑ Other (Describe): | Fee: $ | |
| ❑ Oath/Affirmation | ❑ Acknowledgment | | Travel: $ | |

| Type of Document | Date of Document | Witness(es) Present | Other Signer(s) Present | Right Thumbprint of Signer |
| | | ❑ Yes ❑ No | ❑ Yes ❑ No | |

| Witness: Printed Name | Address/Phone | Signature of Witness | |

| Comments; Additional Information: | If Notarization Failed or Refused, Give Reason: |
| | ❑ Insufficient ID ❑ Signer Confused ❑ Other (Explain in Comments Field) |

29

| Printed Name of Signer: | Signer's Signature: | Time AM/PM: _____ |
| | | Date Notarized: _____ |

| Signer's Complete Address: | City | State | Zip | Phone |
| | | | | |

Identification by: ❑ Identification Card   Issued By: _____ I.D. # _____

❑ Personal Knowledge ❑ Credible Witness(es) Type of I.D.: _____ Expiration Date: _____ Date of Birth: _____

| Type of Notarial Act: | ❑ Verbal Ceremony Performed | ❑ Other (Describe): | Fee: $ | |
| ❑ Oath/Affirmation | ❑ Acknowledgment | | Travel: $ | |

| Type of Document | Date of Document | Witness(es) Present | Other Signer(s) Present | Right Thumbprint of Signer |
| | | ❑ Yes ❑ No | ❑ Yes ❑ No | |

| Witness: Printed Name | Address/Phone | Signature of Witness | |

| Comments; Additional Information: | If Notarization Failed or Refused, Give Reason: |
| | ❑ Insufficient ID ❑ Signer Confused ❑ Other (Explain in Comments Field) |

30

| Printed Name of Signer: | Signer's Signature: | Time AM/PM: _____ |
| | | Date Notarized: _____ |

| Signer's Complete Address: | City | State | Zip | Phone |
| | | | | |

Identification by: ❑ Identification Card   Issued By: _____ I.D. # _____

❑ Personal Knowledge ❑ Credible Witness(es) Type of I.D.: _____ Expiration Date: _____ Date of Birth: _____

| Type of Notarial Act: | ❑ Verbal Ceremony Performed | ❑ Other (Describe): | Fee: $ | |
| ❑ Oath/Affirmation | ❑ Acknowledgment | | Travel: $ | |

| Type of Document | Date of Document | Witness(es) Present | Other Signer(s) Present | Right Thumbprint of Signer |
| | | ❑ Yes ❑ No | ❑ Yes ❑ No | |

| Witness: Printed Name | Address/Phone | Signature of Witness | |

| Comments; Additional Information: | If Notarization Failed or Refused, Give Reason: |
| | ❑ Insufficient ID ❑ Signer Confused ❑ Other (Explain in Comments Field) |

31

Printed Name of Signer:

Signer's Signature:

Time AM/PM: _____

Date Notarized: _____

Signer's Complete Address: City   State   Zip   Phone

Identification by: ❏ Identification Card   Issued By: _____   I.D. # _____

❏ Personal Knowledge   ❏ Credible Witness(es)   Type of I.D.: _____   Expiration Date: _____   Date of Birth: _____

Type of Notarial Act: ❏ Verbal Ceremony Performed   ❏ Other (Describe):   Fee: $ Travel: $

❏ Oath/Affirmation   ❏ Acknowledgment

Type of Document   Date of Document   Witness(es) Present   Other Signer(s) Present
❏ Yes ❏ No   ❏ Yes ❏ No

Witness: Printed Name   Address/Phone   Signature of Witness

Right Thumbprint of Signer

Comments; Additional Information: If Notarization Failed or Refused, Give Reason:

❏ Insufficient ID   ❏ Signer Confused   ❏ Other (Explain in Comments Field)

32

Printed Name of Signer:

Signer's Signature:

Time AM/PM: _____

Date Notarized: _____

Signer's Complete Address: City   State   Zip   Phone

Identification by: ❏ Identification Card   Issued By: _____   I.D. # _____

❏ Personal Knowledge   ❏ Credible Witness(es)   Type of I.D.: _____   Expiration Date: _____   Date of Birth: _____

Type of Notarial Act: ❏ Verbal Ceremony Performed   ❏ Other (Describe):   Fee: $ Travel: $

❏ Oath/Affirmation   ❏ Acknowledgment

Type of Document   Date of Document   Witness(es) Present   Other Signer(s) Present
❏ Yes ❏ No   ❏ Yes ❏ No

Witness: Printed Name   Address/Phone   Signature of Witness

Right Thumbprint of Signer

Comments; Additional Information: If Notarization Failed or Refused, Give Reason:

❏ Insufficient ID   ❏ Signer Confused   ❏ Other (Explain in Comments Field)

33

Printed Name of Signer:

Signer's Signature:

Time AM/PM: _____

Date Notarized: _____

Signer's Complete Address: City   State   Zip   Phone

Identification by: ❏ Identification Card   Issued By: _____   I.D. # _____

❏ Personal Knowledge   ❏ Credible Witness(es)   Type of I.D.: _____   Expiration Date: _____   Date of Birth: _____

Type of Notarial Act: ❏ Verbal Ceremony Performed   ❏ Other (Describe):   Fee: $ Travel: $

❏ Oath/Affirmation   ❏ Acknowledgment

Type of Document   Date of Document   Witness(es) Present   Other Signer(s) Present
❏ Yes ❏ No   ❏ Yes ❏ No

Witness: Printed Name   Address/Phone   Signature of Witness

Right Thumbprint of Signer

Comments; Additional Information: If Notarization Failed or Refused, Give Reason:

❏ Insufficient ID   ❏ Signer Confused   ❏ Other (Explain in Comments Field)

34

Printed Name of Signer:

Signer's Signature:

Time AM/PM: _____

Date Notarized: _____

Signer's Complete Address: City State Zip Phone

Identification by: ❑ Identification Card Issued By: _____ I.D. # _____

❑ Personal Knowledge ❑ Credible Witness(es) Type of I.D.: _____ Expiration Date: _____ Date of Birth: _____

Type of Notarial Act: ❑ Verbal Ceremony Performed ❑ Other (Describe): Fee: $ Travel: $

❑ Oath/Affirmation ❑ Acknowledgment

Right Thumbprint of Signer

Type of Document Date of Document Witness(es) Present ❑ Yes ❑ No Other Signer(s) Present ❑ Yes ❑ No

Witness: Printed Name Address/Phone Signature of Witness

Comments; Additional Information:

If Notarization Failed or Refused, Give Reason:

❑ Insufficient ID ❑ Signer Confused ❑ Other (Explain in Comments Field)

35

Printed Name of Signer:

Signer's Signature:

Time AM/PM: _____

Date Notarized: _____

Signer's Complete Address: City State Zip Phone

Identification by: ❑ Identification Card Issued By: _____ I.D. # _____

❑ Personal Knowledge ❑ Credible Witness(es) Type of I.D.: _____ Expiration Date: _____ Date of Birth: _____

Type of Notarial Act: ❑ Verbal Ceremony Performed ❑ Other (Describe): Fee: $ Travel: $

❑ Oath/Affirmation ❑ Acknowledgment

Right Thumbprint of Signer

Type of Document Date of Document Witness(es) Present ❑ Yes ❑ No Other Signer(s) Present ❑ Yes ❑ No

Witness: Printed Name Address/Phone Signature of Witness

Comments; Additional Information:

If Notarization Failed or Refused, Give Reason:

❑ Insufficient ID ❑ Signer Confused ❑ Other (Explain in Comments Field)

36

Printed Name of Signer:

Signer's Signature:

Time AM/PM: _____

Date Notarized: _____

Signer's Complete Address: City State Zip Phone

Identification by: ❑ Identification Card Issued By: _____ I.D. # _____

❑ Personal Knowledge ❑ Credible Witness(es) Type of I.D.: _____ Expiration Date: _____ Date of Birth: _____

Type of Notarial Act: ❑ Verbal Ceremony Performed ❑ Other (Describe): Fee: $ Travel: $

❑ Oath/Affirmation ❑ Acknowledgment

Right Thumbprint of Signer

Type of Document Date of Document Witness(es) Present ❑ Yes ❑ No Other Signer(s) Present ❑ Yes ❑ No

Witness: Printed Name Address/Phone Signature of Witness

Comments; Additional Information:

If Notarization Failed or Refused, Give Reason:

❑ Insufficient ID ❑ Signer Confused ❑ Other (Explain in Comments Field)

37

Printed Name of Signer:	Signer's Signature:	Time AM/PM: _____ Date Notarized: _____

Signer's Complete Address: City   State   Zip   Phone

Identification by: ❑ Identification Card   Issued By: _____ I.D. # _____

❑ Personal Knowledge   ❑ Credible Witness(es)   Type of I.D.: _____ Expiration Date: _____ Date of Birth: _____

Type of Notarial Act: ❑ Verbal Ceremony Performed   ❑ Other (Describe):   Fee: $

❑ Oath/Affirmation   ❑ Acknowledgment   Travel: $

Right Thumbprint of Signer

Type of Document   Date of Document   Witness(es) Present ❑ Yes ❑ No   Other Signer(s) Present ❑ Yes ❑ No

Witness: Printed Name   Address/Phone   Signature of Witness

Comments; Additional Information:

If Notarization Failed or Refused, Give Reason:

❑ Insufficient ID   ❑ Signer Confused   ❑ Other (Explain in Comments Field)

38

Printed Name of Signer:	Signer's Signature:	Time AM/PM: _____ Date Notarized: _____

Signer's Complete Address: City   State   Zip   Phone

Identification by: ❑ Identification Card   Issued By: _____ I.D. # _____

❑ Personal Knowledge   ❑ Credible Witness(es)   Type of I.D.: _____ Expiration Date: _____ Date of Birth: _____

Type of Notarial Act: ❑ Verbal Ceremony Performed   ❑ Other (Describe):   Fee: $

❑ Oath/Affirmation   ❑ Acknowledgment   Travel: $

Right Thumbprint of Signer

Type of Document   Date of Document   Witness(es) Present ❑ Yes ❑ No   Other Signer(s) Present ❑ Yes ❑ No

Witness: Printed Name   Address/Phone   Signature of Witness

Comments; Additional Information:

If Notarization Failed or Refused, Give Reason:

❑ Insufficient ID   ❑ Signer Confused   ❑ Other (Explain in Comments Field)

39

Printed Name of Signer:	Signer's Signature:	Time AM/PM: _____ Date Notarized: _____

Signer's Complete Address: City   State   Zip   Phone

Identification by: ❑ Identification Card   Issued By: _____ I.D. # _____

❑ Personal Knowledge   ❑ Credible Witness(es)   Type of I.D.: _____ Expiration Date: _____ Date of Birth: _____

Type of Notarial Act: ❑ Verbal Ceremony Performed   ❑ Other (Describe):   Fee: $

❑ Oath/Affirmation   ❑ Acknowledgment   Travel: $

Right Thumbprint of Signer

Type of Document   Date of Document   Witness(es) Present ❑ Yes ❑ No   Other Signer(s) Present ❑ Yes ❑ No

Witness: Printed Name   Address/Phone   Signature of Witness

Comments; Additional Information:

If Notarization Failed or Refused, Give Reason:

❑ Insufficient ID   ❑ Signer Confused   ❑ Other (Explain in Comments Field)

40

| Printed Name of Signer: | Signer's Signature: | Time AM/PM: _____ |
| | | Date Notarized: _____ |

Signer's Complete Address: City   State   Zip   Phone

Identification by: ❑ Identification Card   Issued By: _____   I.D. # _____

❑ Personal Knowledge   ❑ Credible Witness(es)   Type of I.D.: _____   Expiration Date: _____   Date of Birth: _____

Type of Notarial Act: ❑ Verbal Ceremony Performed   ❑ Other (Describe):   Fee: $

❑ Oath/Affirmation   ❑ Acknowledgment   Travel: $

Type of Document   Date of Document   Witness(es) Present   Other Signer(s) Present

    ❑ Yes ❑ No   ❑ Yes ❑ No

Witness: Printed Name   Address/Phone   Signature of Witness

Right Thumbprint of Signer

Comments; Additional Information: If Notarization Failed or Refused, Give Reason:

❑ Insufficient ID   ❑ Signer Confused   ❑ Other (Explain in Comments Field)

41

| Printed Name of Signer: | Signer's Signature: | Time AM/PM: _____ |
| | | Date Notarized: _____ |

Signer's Complete Address: City   State   Zip   Phone

Identification by: ❑ Identification Card   Issued By: _____   I.D. # _____

❑ Personal Knowledge   ❑ Credible Witness(es)   Type of I.D.: _____   Expiration Date: _____   Date of Birth: _____

Type of Notarial Act: ❑ Verbal Ceremony Performed   ❑ Other (Describe):   Fee: $

❑ Oath/Affirmation   ❑ Acknowledgment   Travel: $

Type of Document   Date of Document   Witness(es) Present   Other Signer(s) Present

    ❑ Yes ❑ No   ❑ Yes ❑ No

Witness: Printed Name   Address/Phone   Signature of Witness

Right Thumbprint of Signer

Comments; Additional Information: If Notarization Failed or Refused, Give Reason:

❑ Insufficient ID   ❑ Signer Confused   ❑ Other (Explain in Comments Field)

42

| Printed Name of Signer: | Signer's Signature: | Time AM/PM: _____ |
| | | Date Notarized: _____ |

Signer's Complete Address: City   State   Zip   Phone

Identification by: ❑ Identification Card   Issued By: _____   I.D. # _____

❑ Personal Knowledge   ❑ Credible Witness(es)   Type of I.D.: _____   Expiration Date: _____   Date of Birth: _____

Type of Notarial Act: ❑ Verbal Ceremony Performed   ❑ Other (Describe):   Fee: $

❑ Oath/Affirmation   ❑ Acknowledgment   Travel: $

Type of Document   Date of Document   Witness(es) Present   Other Signer(s) Present

    ❑ Yes ❑ No   ❑ Yes ❑ No

Witness: Printed Name   Address/Phone   Signature of Witness

Right Thumbprint of Signer

Comments; Additional Information: If Notarization Failed or Refused, Give Reason:

❑ Insufficient ID   ❑ Signer Confused   ❑ Other (Explain in Comments Field)

43

Printed Name of Signer:

Signer's Signature:

Time AM/PM: _____
Date Notarized: _____

Signer's Complete Address:

City

State Zip

Phone

Identification by: ❏ Identification Card Issued By: _____ I.D. # _____

❏ Personal Knowledge ❏ Credible Witness(es) Type of I.D.: _____ Expiration Date: _____ Date of Birth: _____

Type of Notarial Act: ❏ Verbal Ceremony Performed ❏ Other (Describe):

❏ Oath/Affirmation ❏ Acknowledgment

Fee: $
Travel: $

Type of Document

Date of Document

Witness(es) Present
❏ Yes ❏ No

Other Signer(s) Present
❏ Yes ❏ No

Right Thumbprint of Signer

Witness: Printed Name

Address/Phone

Signature of Witness

Comments; Additional Information:

If Notarization Failed or Refused, Give Reason:

❏ Insufficient ID ❏ Signer Confused ❏ Other (Explain in Comments Field)

44

Printed Name of Signer:

Signer's Signature:

Time AM/PM: _____
Date Notarized: _____

Signer's Complete Address:

City

State Zip

Phone

Identification by: ❏ Identification Card Issued By: _____ I.D. # _____

❏ Personal Knowledge ❏ Credible Witness(es) Type of I.D.: _____ Expiration Date: _____ Date of Birth: _____

Type of Notarial Act: ❏ Verbal Ceremony Performed ❏ Other (Describe):

❏ Oath/Affirmation ❏ Acknowledgment

Fee: $
Travel: $

Type of Document

Date of Document

Witness(es) Present
❏ Yes ❏ No

Other Signer(s) Present
❏ Yes ❏ No

Right Thumbprint of Signer

Witness: Printed Name

Address/Phone

Signature of Witness

Comments; Additional Information:

If Notarization Failed or Refused, Give Reason:

❏ Insufficient ID ❏ Signer Confused ❏ Other (Explain in Comments Field)

45

Printed Name of Signer:

Signer's Signature:

Time AM/PM: _____
Date Notarized: _____

Signer's Complete Address:

City

State Zip

Phone

Identification by: ❏ Identification Card Issued By: _____ I.D. # _____

❏ Personal Knowledge ❏ Credible Witness(es) Type of I.D.: _____ Expiration Date: _____ Date of Birth: _____

Type of Notarial Act: ❏ Verbal Ceremony Performed ❏ Other (Describe):

❏ Oath/Affirmation ❏ Acknowledgment

Fee: $
Travel: $

Type of Document

Date of Document

Witness(es) Present
❏ Yes ❏ No

Other Signer(s) Present
❏ Yes ❏ No

Right Thumbprint of Signer

Witness: Printed Name

Address/Phone

Signature of Witness

Comments; Additional Information:

If Notarization Failed or Refused, Give Reason:

❏ Insufficient ID ❏ Signer Confused ❏ Other (Explain in Comments Field)

46

| Printed Name of Signer: | Signer's Signature: | Time AM/PM: _____ |
| | | Date Notarized: _____ |

| Signer's Complete Address: | City | State | Zip | Phone |

Identification by: ❑ Identification Card   Issued By: _____   I.D. # _____

❑ Personal Knowledge   ❑ Credible Witness(es)   Type of I.D.: _____   Expiration Date: _____   Date of Birth: _____

| Type of Notarial Act: | ❑ Verbal Ceremony Performed | ❑ Other (Describe): | Fee: $ | |
| ❑ Oath/Affirmation | ❑ Acknowledgment | | Travel: $ | Right Thumbprint of Signer |

| Type of Document | Date of Document | Witness(es) Present | Other Signer(s) Present | |
| | | ❑ Yes ❑ No | ❑ Yes ❑ No | |

| Witness: Printed Name | Address/Phone | Signature of Witness | |

Comments; Additional Information:

If Notarization Failed or Refused, Give Reason:

❑ Insufficient ID   ❑ Signer Confused   ❑ Other (Explain in Comments Field)

47

| Printed Name of Signer: | Signer's Signature: | Time AM/PM: _____ |
| | | Date Notarized: _____ |

| Signer's Complete Address: | City | State | Zip | Phone |

Identification by: ❑ Identification Card   Issued By: _____   I.D. # _____

❑ Personal Knowledge   ❑ Credible Witness(es)   Type of I.D.: _____   Expiration Date: _____   Date of Birth: _____

| Type of Notarial Act: | ❑ Verbal Ceremony Performed | ❑ Other (Describe): | Fee: $ | |
| ❑ Oath/Affirmation | ❑ Acknowledgment | | Travel: $ | Right Thumbprint of Signer |

| Type of Document | Date of Document | Witness(es) Present | Other Signer(s) Present | |
| | | ❑ Yes ❑ No | ❑ Yes ❑ No | |

| Witness: Printed Name | Address/Phone | Signature of Witness | |

Comments; Additional Information:

If Notarization Failed or Refused, Give Reason:

❑ Insufficient ID   ❑ Signer Confused   ❑ Other (Explain in Comments Field)

48

| Printed Name of Signer: | Signer's Signature: | Time AM/PM: _____ |
| | | Date Notarized: _____ |

| Signer's Complete Address: | City | State | Zip | Phone |

Identification by: ❑ Identification Card   Issued By: _____   I.D. # _____

❑ Personal Knowledge   ❑ Credible Witness(es)   Type of I.D.: _____   Expiration Date: _____   Date of Birth: _____

| Type of Notarial Act: | ❑ Verbal Ceremony Performed | ❑ Other (Describe): | Fee: $ | |
| ❑ Oath/Affirmation | ❑ Acknowledgment | | Travel: $ | Right Thumbprint of Signer |

| Type of Document | Date of Document | Witness(es) Present | Other Signer(s) Present | |
| | | ❑ Yes ❑ No | ❑ Yes ❑ No | |

| Witness: Printed Name | Address/Phone | Signature of Witness | |

Comments; Additional Information:

If Notarization Failed or Refused, Give Reason:

❑ Insufficient ID   ❑ Signer Confused   ❑ Other (Explain in Comments Field)

49

| Printed Name of Signer: | Signer's Signature: | Time AM/PM: _____ |
| | | Date Notarized: _____ |

Signer's Complete Address: City   State   Zip   Phone

Identification by: ❏ Identification Card   Issued By: _____   I.D. # _____

❏ Personal Knowledge   ❏ Credible Witness(es)   Type of I.D.: _____   Expiration Date: _____   Date of Birth: _____

Type of Notarial Act: ❏ Verbal Ceremony Performed   ❏ Other (Describe):   Fee: $

❏ Oath/Affirmation   ❏ Acknowledgment   Travel: $

Type of Document   Date of Document   Witness(es) Present   Other Signer(s) Present

❏ Yes ❏ No   ❏ Yes ❏ No

Witness: Printed Name   Address/Phone   Signature of Witness

Right Thumbprint of Signer

Comments; Additional Information: If Notarization Failed or Refused, Give Reason:

❏ Insufficient ID   ❏ Signer Confused   ❏ Other (Explain in Comments Field)

50

| Printed Name of Signer: | Signer's Signature: | Time AM/PM: _____ |
| | | Date Notarized: _____ |

Signer's Complete Address: City   State   Zip   Phone

Identification by: ❏ Identification Card   Issued By: _____   I.D. # _____

❏ Personal Knowledge   ❏ Credible Witness(es)   Type of I.D.: _____   Expiration Date: _____   Date of Birth: _____

Type of Notarial Act: ❏ Verbal Ceremony Performed   ❏ Other (Describe):   Fee: $

❏ Oath/Affirmation   ❏ Acknowledgment   Travel: $

Type of Document   Date of Document   Witness(es) Present   Other Signer(s) Present

❏ Yes ❏ No   ❏ Yes ❏ No

Witness: Printed Name   Address/Phone   Signature of Witness

Right Thumbprint of Signer

Comments; Additional Information: If Notarization Failed or Refused, Give Reason:

❏ Insufficient ID   ❏ Signer Confused   ❏ Other (Explain in Comments Field)

51

| Printed Name of Signer: | Signer's Signature: | Time AM/PM: _____ |
| | | Date Notarized: _____ |

Signer's Complete Address: City   State   Zip   Phone

Identification by: ❏ Identification Card   Issued By: _____   I.D. # _____

❏ Personal Knowledge   ❏ Credible Witness(es)   Type of I.D.: _____   Expiration Date: _____   Date of Birth: _____

Type of Notarial Act: ❏ Verbal Ceremony Performed   ❏ Other (Describe):   Fee: $

❏ Oath/Affirmation   ❏ Acknowledgment   Travel: $

Type of Document   Date of Document   Witness(es) Present   Other Signer(s) Present

❏ Yes ❏ No   ❏ Yes ❏ No

Witness: Printed Name   Address/Phone   Signature of Witness

Right Thumbprint of Signer

Comments; Additional Information: If Notarization Failed or Refused, Give Reason:

❏ Insufficient ID   ❏ Signer Confused   ❏ Other (Explain in Comments Field)

52

| Printed Name of Signer: | Signer's Signature: | Time AM/PM: _____ |
| | | Date Notarized: _____ |

| Signer's Complete Address: | City | State | Zip | Phone |

Identification by: ❑ Identification Card   Issued By: _____   I.D. # _____

❑ Personal Knowledge   ❑ Credible Witness(es)   Type of I.D.: _____   Expiration Date: _____   Date of Birth: _____

| Type of Notarial Act: | ❑ Verbal Ceremony Performed | ❑ Other (Describe): | Fee: $ | |
| ❑ Oath/Affirmation | ❑ Acknowledgment | | Travel: $ | |

| Type of Document | Date of Document | Witness(es) Present | Other Signer(s) Present | Right Thumbprint of Signer |
| | | ❑ Yes ❑ No | ❑ Yes ❑ No | |

| Witness: Printed Name | Address/Phone | Signature of Witness | |

Comments; Additional Information:

If Notarization Failed or Refused, Give Reason:

❑ Insufficient ID   ❑ Signer Confused   ❑ Other (Explain in Comments Field)

53

| Printed Name of Signer: | Signer's Signature: | Time AM/PM: _____ |
| | | Date Notarized: _____ |

| Signer's Complete Address: | City | State | Zip | Phone |

Identification by: ❑ Identification Card   Issued By: _____   I.D. # _____

❑ Personal Knowledge   ❑ Credible Witness(es)   Type of I.D.: _____   Expiration Date: _____   Date of Birth: _____

| Type of Notarial Act: | ❑ Verbal Ceremony Performed | ❑ Other (Describe): | Fee: $ | |
| ❑ Oath/Affirmation | ❑ Acknowledgment | | Travel: $ | |

| Type of Document | Date of Document | Witness(es) Present | Other Signer(s) Present | Right Thumbprint of Signer |
| | | ❑ Yes ❑ No | ❑ Yes ❑ No | |

| Witness: Printed Name | Address/Phone | Signature of Witness | |

Comments; Additional Information:

If Notarization Failed or Refused, Give Reason:

❑ Insufficient ID   ❑ Signer Confused   ❑ Other (Explain in Comments Field)

54

| Printed Name of Signer: | Signer's Signature: | Time AM/PM: _____ |
| | | Date Notarized: _____ |

| Signer's Complete Address: | City | State | Zip | Phone |

Identification by: ❑ Identification Card   Issued By: _____   I.D. # _____

❑ Personal Knowledge   ❑ Credible Witness(es)   Type of I.D.: _____   Expiration Date: _____   Date of Birth: _____

| Type of Notarial Act: | ❑ Verbal Ceremony Performed | ❑ Other (Describe): | Fee: $ | |
| ❑ Oath/Affirmation | ❑ Acknowledgment | | Travel: $ | |

| Type of Document | Date of Document | Witness(es) Present | Other Signer(s) Present | Right Thumbprint of Signer |
| | | ❑ Yes ❑ No | ❑ Yes ❑ No | |

| Witness: Printed Name | Address/Phone | Signature of Witness | |

Comments; Additional Information:

If Notarization Failed or Refused, Give Reason:

❑ Insufficient ID   ❑ Signer Confused   ❑ Other (Explain in Comments Field)

55

| Printed Name of Signer: | Signer's Signature: | Time AM/PM: _____ |
| | | Date Notarized: _____ |

| Signer's Complete Address: | City | State | Zip | Phone |

| Identification by: | ❑ Identification Card | Issued By: _____ | I.D. # _____ |
| ❑ Personal Knowledge | ❑ Credible Witness(es) | Type of I.D.: _____ | Expiration Date: _____ | Date of Birth: _____ |

| Type of Notarial Act: | ❑ Verbal Ceremony Performed | ❑ Other (Describe): | Fee: $ | |
| ❑ Oath/Affirmation | ❑ Acknowledgment | | Travel: $ | Right Thumbprint of Signer |

| Type of Document | Date of Document | Witness(es) Present | Other Signer(s) Present | |
| | | ❑ Yes ❑ No | ❑ Yes ❑ No | |

| Witness: Printed Name | Address/Phone | Signature of Witness | |

| Comments; Additional Information: | If Notarization Failed or Refused, Give Reason: |
| | ❑ Insufficient ID ❑ Signer Confused ❑ Other (Explain in Comments Field) |

56

| Printed Name of Signer: | Signer's Signature: | Time AM/PM: _____ |
| | | Date Notarized: _____ |

| Signer's Complete Address: | City | State | Zip | Phone |

| Identification by: | ❑ Identification Card | Issued By: _____ | I.D. # _____ |
| ❑ Personal Knowledge | ❑ Credible Witness(es) | Type of I.D.: _____ | Expiration Date: _____ | Date of Birth: _____ |

| Type of Notarial Act: | ❑ Verbal Ceremony Performed | ❑ Other (Describe): | Fee: $ | |
| ❑ Oath/Affirmation | ❑ Acknowledgment | | Travel: $ | Right Thumbprint of Signer |

| Type of Document | Date of Document | Witness(es) Present | Other Signer(s) Present | |
| | | ❑ Yes ❑ No | ❑ Yes ❑ No | |

| Witness: Printed Name | Address/Phone | Signature of Witness | |

| Comments; Additional Information: | If Notarization Failed or Refused, Give Reason: |
| | ❑ Insufficient ID ❑ Signer Confused ❑ Other (Explain in Comments Field) |

57

| Printed Name of Signer: | Signer's Signature: | Time AM/PM: _____ |
| | | Date Notarized: _____ |

| Signer's Complete Address: | City | State | Zip | Phone |

| Identification by: | ❑ Identification Card | Issued By: _____ | I.D. # _____ |
| ❑ Personal Knowledge | ❑ Credible Witness(es) | Type of I.D.: _____ | Expiration Date: _____ | Date of Birth: _____ |

| Type of Notarial Act: | ❑ Verbal Ceremony Performed | ❑ Other (Describe): | Fee: $ | |
| ❑ Oath/Affirmation | ❑ Acknowledgment | | Travel: $ | Right Thumbprint of Signer |

| Type of Document | Date of Document | Witness(es) Present | Other Signer(s) Present | |
| | | ❑ Yes ❑ No | ❑ Yes ❑ No | |

| Witness: Printed Name | Address/Phone | Signature of Witness | |

| Comments; Additional Information: | If Notarization Failed or Refused, Give Reason: |
| | ❑ Insufficient ID ❑ Signer Confused ❑ Other (Explain in Comments Field) |

Printed Name of Signer:	Signer's Signature:	Time AM/PM: _____	**58**
		Date Notarized: _____	

Signer's Complete Address: City   State   Zip   Phone

Identification by: ❏ Identification Card   Issued By: _____   I.D. #_____

❏ Personal Knowledge   ❏ Credible Witness(es)   Type of I.D.: _____   Expiration Date: _____   Date of Birth: _____

Type of Notarial Act: ❏ Verbal Ceremony Performed   ❏ Other (Describe):   Fee: $

❏ Oath/Affirmation   ❏ Acknowledgment   Travel: $

Type of Document   Date of Document   Witness(es) Present   Other Signer(s) Present

❏ Yes ❏ No   ❏ Yes ❏ No

Right Thumbprint of Signer

Witness: Printed Name   Address/Phone   Signature of Witness

Comments; Additional Information: If Notarization Failed or Refused, Give Reason:

❏ Insufficient ID   ❏ Signer Confused   ❏ Other (Explain in Comments Field)

Printed Name of Signer:	Signer's Signature:	Time AM/PM: _____	**59**
		Date Notarized: _____	

Signer's Complete Address: City   State   Zip   Phone

Identification by: ❏ Identification Card   Issued By: _____   I.D. #_____

❏ Personal Knowledge   ❏ Credible Witness(es)   Type of I.D.: _____   Expiration Date: _____   Date of Birth: _____

Type of Notarial Act: ❏ Verbal Ceremony Performed   ❏ Other (Describe):   Fee: $

❏ Oath/Affirmation   ❏ Acknowledgment   Travel: $

Type of Document   Date of Document   Witness(es) Present   Other Signer(s) Present

❏ Yes ❏ No   ❏ Yes ❏ No

Right Thumbprint of Signer

Witness: Printed Name   Address/Phone   Signature of Witness

Comments; Additional Information: If Notarization Failed or Refused, Give Reason:

❏ Insufficient ID   ❏ Signer Confused   ❏ Other (Explain in Comments Field)

Printed Name of Signer:	Signer's Signature:	Time AM/PM: _____	**60**
		Date Notarized: _____	

Signer's Complete Address: City   State   Zip   Phone

Identification by: ❏ Identification Card   Issued By: _____   I.D. #_____

❏ Personal Knowledge   ❏ Credible Witness(es)   Type of I.D.: _____   Expiration Date: _____   Date of Birth: _____

Type of Notarial Act: ❏ Verbal Ceremony Performed   ❏ Other (Describe):   Fee: $

❏ Oath/Affirmation   ❏ Acknowledgment   Travel: $

Type of Document   Date of Document   Witness(es) Present   Other Signer(s) Present

❏ Yes ❏ No   ❏ Yes ❏ No

Right Thumbprint of Signer

Witness: Printed Name   Address/Phone   Signature of Witness

Comments; Additional Information: If Notarization Failed or Refused, Give Reason:

❏ Insufficient ID   ❏ Signer Confused   ❏ Other (Explain in Comments Field)

61

Printed Name of Signer:

Signer's Signature:

Time AM/PM: _____

Date Notarized: _____

Signer's Complete Address: City   State   Zip   Phone

Identification by: ❏ Identification Card   Issued By: _____   I.D. #_____

❏ Personal Knowledge   ❏ Credible Witness(es)   Type of I.D.:_____   Expiration Date: _____   Date of Birth: _____

Type of Notarial Act: ❏ Verbal Ceremony Performed   ❏ Other (Describe):   Fee: $
❏ Oath/Affirmation   ❏ Acknowledgment   Travel: $

Type of Document   Date of Document   Witness(es) Present   Other Signer(s) Present
                        ❏ Yes ❏ No   ❏ Yes ❏ No

Witness: Printed Name   Address/Phone   Signature of Witness

Right Thumbprint of Signer

Comments; Additional Information: If Notarization Failed or Refused, Give Reason:

❏ Insufficient ID   ❏ Signer Confused   ❏ Other (Explain in Comments Field)

62

Printed Name of Signer:

Signer's Signature:

Time AM/PM: _____

Date Notarized: _____

Signer's Complete Address: City   State   Zip   Phone

Identification by: ❏ Identification Card   Issued By: _____   I.D. #_____

❏ Personal Knowledge   ❏ Credible Witness(es)   Type of I.D.:_____   Expiration Date: _____   Date of Birth: _____

Type of Notarial Act: ❏ Verbal Ceremony Performed   ❏ Other (Describe):   Fee: $
❏ Oath/Affirmation   ❏ Acknowledgment   Travel: $

Type of Document   Date of Document   Witness(es) Present   Other Signer(s) Present
                        ❏ Yes ❏ No   ❏ Yes ❏ No

Witness: Printed Name   Address/Phone   Signature of Witness

Right Thumbprint of Signer

Comments; Additional Information: If Notarization Failed or Refused, Give Reason:

❏ Insufficient ID   ❏ Signer Confused   ❏ Other (Explain in Comments Field)

63

Printed Name of Signer:

Signer's Signature:

Time AM/PM: _____

Date Notarized: _____

Signer's Complete Address: City   State   Zip   Phone

Identification by: ❏ Identification Card   Issued By: _____   I.D. #_____

❏ Personal Knowledge   ❏ Credible Witness(es)   Type of I.D.:_____   Expiration Date: _____   Date of Birth: _____

Type of Notarial Act: ❏ Verbal Ceremony Performed   ❏ Other (Describe):   Fee: $
❏ Oath/Affirmation   ❏ Acknowledgment   Travel: $

Type of Document   Date of Document   Witness(es) Present   Other Signer(s) Present
                        ❏ Yes ❏ No   ❏ Yes ❏ No

Witness: Printed Name   Address/Phone   Signature of Witness

Right Thumbprint of Signer

Comments; Additional Information: If Notarization Failed or Refused, Give Reason:

❏ Insufficient ID   ❏ Signer Confused   ❏ Other (Explain in Comments Field)

64

| Printed Name of Signer: | Signer's Signature: | Time AM/PM: _____ |
| | | Date Notarized: _____ |

| Signer's Complete Address: | City | State | Zip | Phone |

Identification by: ❏ Identification Card Issued By: _____ I.D. # _____

❏ Personal Knowledge ❏ Credible Witness(es) Type of I.D.: _____ Expiration Date: _____ Date of Birth: _____

| Type of Notarial Act: | ❏ Verbal Ceremony Performed | ❏ Other (Describe): | Fee: $ |
| ❏ Oath/Affirmation | ❏ Acknowledgment | | Travel: $ |

| Type of Document | Date of Document | Witness(es) Present ❏ Yes ❏ No | Other Signer(s) Present ❏ Yes ❏ No |

Right Thumbprint of Signer

| Witness: Printed Name | Address/Phone | Signature of Witness |

| Comments; Additional Information: | If Notarization Failed or Refused, Give Reason: |
| | ❏ Insufficient ID ❏ Signer Confused ❏ Other (Explain in Comments Field) |

65

| Printed Name of Signer: | Signer's Signature: | Time AM/PM: _____ |
| | | Date Notarized: _____ |

| Signer's Complete Address: | City | State | Zip | Phone |

Identification by: ❏ Identification Card Issued By: _____ I.D. # _____

❏ Personal Knowledge ❏ Credible Witness(es) Type of I.D.: _____ Expiration Date: _____ Date of Birth: _____

| Type of Notarial Act: | ❏ Verbal Ceremony Performed | ❏ Other (Describe): | Fee: $ |
| ❏ Oath/Affirmation | ❏ Acknowledgment | | Travel: $ |

| Type of Document | Date of Document | Witness(es) Present ❏ Yes ❏ No | Other Signer(s) Present ❏ Yes ❏ No |

Right Thumbprint of Signer

| Witness: Printed Name | Address/Phone | Signature of Witness |

| Comments; Additional Information: | If Notarization Failed or Refused, Give Reason: |
| | ❏ Insufficient ID ❏ Signer Confused ❏ Other (Explain in Comments Field) |

66

| Printed Name of Signer: | Signer's Signature: | Time AM/PM: _____ |
| | | Date Notarized: _____ |

| Signer's Complete Address: | City | State | Zip | Phone |

Identification by: ❏ Identification Card Issued By: _____ I.D. # _____

❏ Personal Knowledge ❏ Credible Witness(es) Type of I.D.: _____ Expiration Date: _____ Date of Birth: _____

| Type of Notarial Act: | ❏ Verbal Ceremony Performed | ❏ Other (Describe): | Fee: $ |
| ❏ Oath/Affirmation | ❏ Acknowledgment | | Travel: $ |

| Type of Document | Date of Document | Witness(es) Present ❏ Yes ❏ No | Other Signer(s) Present ❏ Yes ❏ No |

Right Thumbprint of Signer

| Witness: Printed Name | Address/Phone | Signature of Witness |

| Comments; Additional Information: | If Notarization Failed or Refused, Give Reason: |
| | ❏ Insufficient ID ❏ Signer Confused ❏ Other (Explain in Comments Field) |

67

| Printed Name of Signer: | Signer's Signature: | Time AM/PM: _____ |
| | | Date Notarized: _____ |

Signer's Complete Address: City   State   Zip   Phone

Identification by: ❏ Identification Card   Issued By: _____   I.D. #_____

❏ Personal Knowledge   ❏ Credible Witness(es)   Type of I.D.:_____   Expiration Date: _____   Date of Birth: _____

Type of Notarial Act: ❏ Verbal Ceremony Performed   ❏ Other (Describe):   Fee: $ _____

❏ Oath/Affirmation   ❏ Acknowledgment   Travel: $ _____

Right Thumbprint of Signer

Type of Document   Date of Document   Witness(es) Present ❏ Yes ❏ No   Other Signer(s) Present ❏ Yes ❏ No

Witness: Printed Name   Address/Phone   Signature of Witness

Comments; Additional Information: If Notarization Failed or Refused, Give Reason:

❏ Insufficient ID   ❏ Signer Confused   ❏ Other (Explain in Comments Field)

68

| Printed Name of Signer: | Signer's Signature: | Time AM/PM: _____ |
| | | Date Notarized: _____ |

Signer's Complete Address: City   State   Zip   Phone

Identification by: ❏ Identification Card   Issued By: _____   I.D. #_____

❏ Personal Knowledge   ❏ Credible Witness(es)   Type of I.D.:_____   Expiration Date: _____   Date of Birth: _____

Type of Notarial Act: ❏ Verbal Ceremony Performed   ❏ Other (Describe):   Fee: $ _____

❏ Oath/Affirmation   ❏ Acknowledgment   Travel: $ _____

Right Thumbprint of Signer

Type of Document   Date of Document   Witness(es) Present ❏ Yes ❏ No   Other Signer(s) Present ❏ Yes ❏ No

Witness: Printed Name   Address/Phone   Signature of Witness

Comments; Additional Information: If Notarization Failed or Refused, Give Reason:

❏ Insufficient ID   ❏ Signer Confused   ❏ Other (Explain in Comments Field)

69

| Printed Name of Signer: | Signer's Signature: | Time AM/PM: _____ |
| | | Date Notarized: _____ |

Signer's Complete Address: City   State   Zip   Phone

Identification by: ❏ Identification Card   Issued By: _____   I.D. #_____

❏ Personal Knowledge   ❏ Credible Witness(es)   Type of I.D.:_____   Expiration Date: _____   Date of Birth: _____

Type of Notarial Act: ❏ Verbal Ceremony Performed   ❏ Other (Describe):   Fee: $ _____

❏ Oath/Affirmation   ❏ Acknowledgment   Travel: $ _____

Right Thumbprint of Signer

Type of Document   Date of Document   Witness(es) Present ❏ Yes ❏ No   Other Signer(s) Present ❏ Yes ❏ No

Witness: Printed Name   Address/Phone   Signature of Witness

Comments; Additional Information: If Notarization Failed or Refused, Give Reason:

❏ Insufficient ID   ❏ Signer Confused   ❏ Other (Explain in Comments Field)

Printed Name of Signer: | **Signer's Signature:** | **Time AM/PM:** _____ **70**
Date Notarized: _____

Signer's Complete Address: | **City** | **State** | **Zip** | **Phone**

Identification by: | ❏ Identification Card | **Issued By:** _____ | **I.D. #** _____

❏ **Personal Knowledge** | ❏ Credible Witness(es) | **Type of I.D.:** _____ | **Expiration Date:** _____ | **Date of Birth:** _____

Type of Notarial Act: | ❏ Verbal Ceremony Performed | ❏ Other (Describe): | **Fee: $** | **Right Thumbprint of Signer**
❏ Oath/Affirmation | ❏ Acknowledgment | | **Travel: $**

Type of Document | **Date of Document** | **Witness(es) Present** ❏ Yes ❏ No | **Other Signer(s) Present** ❏ Yes ❏ No

Witness: Printed Name | **Address/Phone** | **Signature of Witness**

Comments; Additional Information: | **If Notarization Failed or Refused, Give Reason:**
❏ Insufficient ID ❏ Signer Confused ❏ Other (Explain in Comments Field)

Printed Name of Signer: | **Signer's Signature:** | **Time AM/PM:** _____ **71**
Date Notarized: _____

Signer's Complete Address: | **City** | **State** | **Zip** | **Phone**

Identification by: | ❏ Identification Card | **Issued By:** _____ | **I.D. #** _____

❏ **Personal Knowledge** | ❏ Credible Witness(es) | **Type of I.D.:** _____ | **Expiration Date:** _____ | **Date of Birth:** _____

Type of Notarial Act: | ❏ Verbal Ceremony Performed | ❏ Other (Describe): | **Fee: $** | **Right Thumbprint of Signer**
❏ Oath/Affirmation | ❏ Acknowledgment | | **Travel: $**

Type of Document | **Date of Document** | **Witness(es) Present** ❏ Yes ❏ No | **Other Signer(s) Present** ❏ Yes ❏ No

Witness: Printed Name | **Address/Phone** | **Signature of Witness**

Comments; Additional Information: | **If Notarization Failed or Refused, Give Reason:**
❏ Insufficient ID ❏ Signer Confused ❏ Other (Explain in Comments Field)

Printed Name of Signer: | **Signer's Signature:** | **Time AM/PM:** _____ **72**
Date Notarized: _____

Signer's Complete Address: | **City** | **State** | **Zip** | **Phone**

Identification by: | ❏ Identification Card | **Issued By:** _____ | **I.D. #** _____

❏ **Personal Knowledge** | ❏ Credible Witness(es) | **Type of I.D.:** _____ | **Expiration Date:** _____ | **Date of Birth:** _____

Type of Notarial Act: | ❏ Verbal Ceremony Performed | ❏ Other (Describe): | **Fee: $** | **Right Thumbprint of Signer**
❏ Oath/Affirmation | ❏ Acknowledgment | | **Travel: $**

Type of Document | **Date of Document** | **Witness(es) Present** ❏ Yes ❏ No | **Other Signer(s) Present** ❏ Yes ❏ No

Witness: Printed Name | **Address/Phone** | **Signature of Witness**

Comments; Additional Information: | **If Notarization Failed or Refused, Give Reason:**
❏ Insufficient ID ❏ Signer Confused ❏ Other (Explain in Comments Field)

73

Printed Name of Signer:

Signer's Signature:

Time AM/PM: _____

Date Notarized: _____

Signer's Complete Address: City   State   Zip   Phone

Identification by: ❏ Identification Card   Issued By: _____   I.D. # _____

❏ Personal Knowledge   ❏ Credible Witness(es)   Type of I.D.: _____   Expiration Date: _____   Date of Birth: _____

Type of Notarial Act: ❏ Verbal Ceremony Performed   ❏ Other (Describe):   Fee: $ Travel: $

❏ Oath/Affirmation   ❏ Acknowledgment

Type of Document   Date of Document   Witness(es) Present   ❏ Yes ❏ No   Other Signer(s) Present   ❏ Yes ❏ No

Right Thumbprint of Signer

Witness: Printed Name   Address/Phone   Signature of Witness

Comments; Additional Information:

If Notarization Failed or Refused, Give Reason:

❏ Insufficient ID   ❏ Signer Confused   ❏ Other (Explain in Comments Field)

74

Printed Name of Signer:

Signer's Signature:

Time AM/PM: _____

Date Notarized: _____

Signer's Complete Address: City   State   Zip   Phone

Identification by: ❏ Identification Card   Issued By: _____   I.D. # _____

❏ Personal Knowledge   ❏ Credible Witness(es)   Type of I.D.: _____   Expiration Date: _____   Date of Birth: _____

Type of Notarial Act: ❏ Verbal Ceremony Performed   ❏ Other (Describe):   Fee: $ Travel: $

❏ Oath/Affirmation   ❏ Acknowledgment

Type of Document   Date of Document   Witness(es) Present   ❏ Yes ❏ No   Other Signer(s) Present   ❏ Yes ❏ No

Right Thumbprint of Signer

Witness: Printed Name   Address/Phone   Signature of Witness

Comments; Additional Information:

If Notarization Failed or Refused, Give Reason:

❏ Insufficient ID   ❏ Signer Confused   ❏ Other (Explain in Comments Field)

75

Printed Name of Signer:

Signer's Signature:

Time AM/PM: _____

Date Notarized: _____

Signer's Complete Address: City   State   Zip   Phone

Identification by: ❏ Identification Card   Issued By: _____   I.D. # _____

❏ Personal Knowledge   ❏ Credible Witness(es)   Type of I.D.: _____   Expiration Date: _____   Date of Birth: _____

Type of Notarial Act: ❏ Verbal Ceremony Performed   ❏ Other (Describe):   Fee: $ Travel: $

❏ Oath/Affirmation   ❏ Acknowledgment

Type of Document   Date of Document   Witness(es) Present   ❏ Yes ❏ No   Other Signer(s) Present   ❏ Yes ❏ No

Right Thumbprint of Signer

Witness: Printed Name   Address/Phone   Signature of Witness

Comments; Additional Information:

If Notarization Failed or Refused, Give Reason:

❏ Insufficient ID   ❏ Signer Confused   ❏ Other (Explain in Comments Field)

76

| Printed Name of Signer: | Signer's Signature: | Time AM/PM: _____ |
| | | Date Notarized: _____ |

Signer's Complete Address: City   State   Zip   Phone

Identification by: ❑ Identification Card   Issued By: _____   I.D. #_____

❑ Personal Knowledge   ❑ Credible Witness(es)   Type of I.D.:_____   Expiration Date: _____   Date of Birth: _____

Type of Notarial Act: ❑ Verbal Ceremony Performed   ❑ Other (Describe):   Fee: $

❑ Oath/Affirmation   ❑ Acknowledgment   Travel: $

Type of Document   Date of Document   Witness(es) Present   Other Signer(s) Present
❑ Yes ❑ No   ❑ Yes ❑ No

Witness: Printed Name   Address/Phone   Signature of Witness

Right Thumbprint of Signer

Comments; Additional Information: If Notarization Failed or Refused, Give Reason:

❑ Insufficient ID   ❑ Signer Confused   ❑ Other (Explain in Comments Field)

77

| Printed Name of Signer: | Signer's Signature: | Time AM/PM: _____ |
| | | Date Notarized: _____ |

Signer's Complete Address: City   State   Zip   Phone

Identification by: ❑ Identification Card   Issued By: _____   I.D. #_____

❑ Personal Knowledge   ❑ Credible Witness(es)   Type of I.D.:_____   Expiration Date: _____   Date of Birth: _____

Type of Notarial Act: ❑ Verbal Ceremony Performed   ❑ Other (Describe):   Fee: $

❑ Oath/Affirmation   ❑ Acknowledgment   Travel: $

Type of Document   Date of Document   Witness(es) Present   Other Signer(s) Present
❑ Yes ❑ No   ❑ Yes ❑ No

Witness: Printed Name   Address/Phone   Signature of Witness

Right Thumbprint of Signer

Comments; Additional Information: If Notarization Failed or Refused, Give Reason:

❑ Insufficient ID   ❑ Signer Confused   ❑ Other (Explain in Comments Field)

78

| Printed Name of Signer: | Signer's Signature: | Time AM/PM: _____ |
| | | Date Notarized: _____ |

Signer's Complete Address: City   State   Zip   Phone

Identification by: ❑ Identification Card   Issued By: _____   I.D. #_____

❑ Personal Knowledge   ❑ Credible Witness(es)   Type of I.D.:_____   Expiration Date: _____   Date of Birth: _____

Type of Notarial Act: ❑ Verbal Ceremony Performed   ❑ Other (Describe):   Fee: $

❑ Oath/Affirmation   ❑ Acknowledgment   Travel: $

Type of Document   Date of Document   Witness(es) Present   Other Signer(s) Present
❑ Yes ❑ No   ❑ Yes ❑ No

Witness: Printed Name   Address/Phone   Signature of Witness

Right Thumbprint of Signer

Comments; Additional Information: If Notarization Failed or Refused, Give Reason:

❑ Insufficient ID   ❑ Signer Confused   ❑ Other (Explain in Comments Field)

79

Printed Name of Signer:

Signer's Signature:

Time AM/PM: _____

Date Notarized: _____

Signer's Complete Address: City   State   Zip   Phone

Identification by: ❏ Identification Card   Issued By: _____   I.D. # _____

❏ Personal Knowledge   ❏ Credible Witness(es)   Type of I.D.: _____   Expiration Date: _____   Date of Birth: _____

Type of Notarial Act: ❏ Verbal Ceremony Performed   ❏ Other (Describe):   Fee: $

❏ Oath/Affirmation   ❏ Acknowledgment   Travel: $

Type of Document   Date of Document   Witness(es) Present   Other Signer(s) Present

❏ Yes ❏ No   ❏ Yes ❏ No

Right Thumbprint of Signer

Witness: Printed Name   Address/Phone   Signature of Witness

Comments; Additional Information: If Notarization Failed or Refused, Give Reason:

❏ Insufficient ID   ❏ Signer Confused   ❏ Other (Explain in Comments Field)

80

Printed Name of Signer:

Signer's Signature:

Time AM/PM: _____

Date Notarized: _____

Signer's Complete Address: City   State   Zip   Phone

Identification by: ❏ Identification Card   Issued By: _____   I.D. # _____

❏ Personal Knowledge   ❏ Credible Witness(es)   Type of I.D.: _____   Expiration Date: _____   Date of Birth: _____

Type of Notarial Act: ❏ Verbal Ceremony Performed   ❏ Other (Describe):   Fee: $

❏ Oath/Affirmation   ❏ Acknowledgment   Travel: $

Type of Document   Date of Document   Witness(es) Present   Other Signer(s) Present

❏ Yes ❏ No   ❏ Yes ❏ No

Right Thumbprint of Signer

Witness: Printed Name   Address/Phone   Signature of Witness

Comments; Additional Information: If Notarization Failed or Refused, Give Reason:

❏ Insufficient ID   ❏ Signer Confused   ❏ Other (Explain in Comments Field)

81

Printed Name of Signer:

Signer's Signature:

Time AM/PM: _____

Date Notarized: _____

Signer's Complete Address: City   State   Zip   Phone

Identification by: ❏ Identification Card   Issued By: _____   I.D. # _____

❏ Personal Knowledge   ❏ Credible Witness(es)   Type of I.D.: _____   Expiration Date: _____   Date of Birth: _____

Type of Notarial Act: ❏ Verbal Ceremony Performed   ❏ Other (Describe):   Fee: $

❏ Oath/Affirmation   ❏ Acknowledgment   Travel: $

Type of Document   Date of Document   Witness(es) Present   Other Signer(s) Present

❏ Yes ❏ No   ❏ Yes ❏ No

Right Thumbprint of Signer

Witness: Printed Name   Address/Phone   Signature of Witness

Comments; Additional Information: If Notarization Failed or Refused, Give Reason:

❏ Insufficient ID   ❏ Signer Confused   ❏ Other (Explain in Comments Field)

82

Printed Name of Signer: Signer's Signature: Time AM/PM: _____
                                                                                Date Notarized: _____

Signer's Complete Address: City   State   Zip   Phone

Identification by: ❏ Identification Card   Issued By: _____   I.D. # _____

❏ Personal Knowledge   ❏ Credible Witness(es)   Type of I.D.: _____ Expiration Date: _____   Date of Birth: _____

Type of Notarial Act: ❏ Verbal Ceremony Performed   ❏ Other (Describe):   Fee: $
❏ Oath/Affirmation   ❏ Acknowledgment   Travel: $

Type of Document   Date of Document   Witness(es) Present   Other Signer(s) Present
                                                ❏ Yes ❏ No   ❏ Yes ❏ No

Witness: Printed Name   Address/Phone   Signature of Witness

Right Thumbprint of Signer

Comments; Additional Information: If Notarization Failed or Refused, Give Reason:

                                                    ❏ Insufficient ID   ❏ Signer Confused   ❏ Other (Explain in Comments Field)

83

Printed Name of Signer: Signer's Signature: Time AM/PM: _____
                                                                                Date Notarized: _____

Signer's Complete Address: City   State   Zip   Phone

Identification by: ❏ Identification Card   Issued By: _____   I.D. # _____

❏ Personal Knowledge   ❏ Credible Witness(es)   Type of I.D.: _____ Expiration Date: _____   Date of Birth: _____

Type of Notarial Act: ❏ Verbal Ceremony Performed   ❏ Other (Describe):   Fee: $
❏ Oath/Affirmation   ❏ Acknowledgment   Travel: $

Type of Document   Date of Document   Witness(es) Present   Other Signer(s) Present
                                                ❏ Yes ❏ No   ❏ Yes ❏ No

Witness: Printed Name   Address/Phone   Signature of Witness

Right Thumbprint of Signer

Comments; Additional Information: If Notarization Failed or Refused, Give Reason:

                                                    ❏ Insufficient ID   ❏ Signer Confused   ❏ Other (Explain in Comments Field)

84

Printed Name of Signer: Signer's Signature: Time AM/PM: _____
                                                                                Date Notarized: _____

Signer's Complete Address: City   State   Zip   Phone

Identification by: ❏ Identification Card   Issued By: _____   I.D. # _____

❏ Personal Knowledge   ❏ Credible Witness(es)   Type of I.D.: _____ Expiration Date: _____   Date of Birth: _____

Type of Notarial Act: ❏ Verbal Ceremony Performed   ❏ Other (Describe):   Fee: $
❏ Oath/Affirmation   ❏ Acknowledgment   Travel: $

Type of Document   Date of Document   Witness(es) Present   Other Signer(s) Present
                                                ❏ Yes ❏ No   ❏ Yes ❏ No

Witness: Printed Name   Address/Phone   Signature of Witness

Right Thumbprint of Signer

Comments; Additional Information: If Notarization Failed or Refused, Give Reason:

                                                    ❏ Insufficient ID   ❏ Signer Confused   ❏ Other (Explain in Comments Field)

85

Printed Name of Signer:

Signer's Signature:

Time AM/PM: _____

Date Notarized: _____

Signer's Complete Address: City   State   Zip   Phone

Identification by: ❏ Identification Card   Issued By: _____   I.D. # _____

❏ Personal Knowledge   ❏ Credible Witness(es)   Type of I.D.: _____   Expiration Date: _____   Date of Birth: _____

Type of Notarial Act: ❏ Verbal Ceremony Performed   ❏ Other (Describe):   Fee: $

❏ Oath/Affirmation   ❏ Acknowledgment   Travel: $

Type of Document   Date of Document   Witness(es) Present   Other Signer(s) Present

❏ Yes ❏ No   ❏ Yes ❏ No

Right Thumbprint of Signer

Witness: Printed Name   Address/Phone   Signature of Witness

Comments; Additional Information: If Notarization Failed or Refused, Give Reason:

❏ Insufficient ID   ❏ Signer Confused   ❏ Other (Explain in Comments Field)

86

Printed Name of Signer:

Signer's Signature:

Time AM/PM: _____

Date Notarized: _____

Signer's Complete Address: City   State   Zip   Phone

Identification by: ❏ Identification Card   Issued By: _____   I.D. # _____

❏ Personal Knowledge   ❏ Credible Witness(es)   Type of I.D.: _____   Expiration Date: _____   Date of Birth: _____

Type of Notarial Act: ❏ Verbal Ceremony Performed   ❏ Other (Describe):   Fee: $

❏ Oath/Affirmation   ❏ Acknowledgment   Travel: $

Type of Document   Date of Document   Witness(es) Present   Other Signer(s) Present

❏ Yes ❏ No   ❏ Yes ❏ No

Right Thumbprint of Signer

Witness: Printed Name   Address/Phone   Signature of Witness

Comments; Additional Information: If Notarization Failed or Refused, Give Reason:

❏ Insufficient ID   ❏ Signer Confused   ❏ Other (Explain in Comments Field)

87

Printed Name of Signer:

Signer's Signature:

Time AM/PM: _____

Date Notarized: _____

Signer's Complete Address: City   State   Zip   Phone

Identification by: ❏ Identification Card   Issued By: _____   I.D. # _____

❏ Personal Knowledge   ❏ Credible Witness(es)   Type of I.D.: _____   Expiration Date: _____   Date of Birth: _____

Type of Notarial Act: ❏ Verbal Ceremony Performed   ❏ Other (Describe):   Fee: $

❏ Oath/Affirmation   ❏ Acknowledgment   Travel: $

Type of Document   Date of Document   Witness(es) Present   Other Signer(s) Present

❏ Yes ❏ No   ❏ Yes ❏ No

Right Thumbprint of Signer

Witness: Printed Name   Address/Phone   Signature of Witness

Comments; Additional Information: If Notarization Failed or Refused, Give Reason:

❏ Insufficient ID   ❏ Signer Confused   ❏ Other (Explain in Comments Field)

88

| Printed Name of Signer: | Signer's Signature: | Time AM/PM: _____ |
| | | Date Notarized: _____ |

| Signer's Complete Address: | City | State | Zip | Phone |

Identification by: ❏ Identification Card   Issued By: _____   I.D. # _____

❏ Personal Knowledge   ❏ Credible Witness(es)   Type of I.D.: _____   Expiration Date: _____   Date of Birth: _____

| Type of Notarial Act: | ❏ Verbal Ceremony Performed | ❏ Other (Describe): | Fee: $ | |
| ❏ Oath/Affirmation | ❏ Acknowledgment | | Travel: $ | Right Thumbprint of Signer |

| Type of Document | Date of Document | Witness(es) Present | Other Signer(s) Present | |
| | | ❏ Yes ❏ No | ❏ Yes ❏ No | |

| Witness: Printed Name | Address/Phone | Signature of Witness | |

Comments; Additional Information:

If Notarization Failed or Refused, Give Reason:

❏ Insufficient ID   ❏ Signer Confused   ❏ Other (Explain in Comments Field)

89

| Printed Name of Signer: | Signer's Signature: | Time AM/PM: _____ |
| | | Date Notarized: _____ |

| Signer's Complete Address: | City | State | Zip | Phone |

Identification by: ❏ Identification Card   Issued By: _____   I.D. # _____

❏ Personal Knowledge   ❏ Credible Witness(es)   Type of I.D.: _____   Expiration Date: _____   Date of Birth: _____

| Type of Notarial Act: | ❏ Verbal Ceremony Performed | ❏ Other (Describe): | Fee: $ | |
| ❏ Oath/Affirmation | ❏ Acknowledgment | | Travel: $ | Right Thumbprint of Signer |

| Type of Document | Date of Document | Witness(es) Present | Other Signer(s) Present | |
| | | ❏ Yes ❏ No | ❏ Yes ❏ No | |

| Witness: Printed Name | Address/Phone | Signature of Witness | |

Comments; Additional Information:

If Notarization Failed or Refused, Give Reason:

❏ Insufficient ID   ❏ Signer Confused   ❏ Other (Explain in Comments Field)

90

| Printed Name of Signer: | Signer's Signature: | Time AM/PM: _____ |
| | | Date Notarized: _____ |

| Signer's Complete Address: | City | State | Zip | Phone |

Identification by: ❏ Identification Card   Issued By: _____   I.D. # _____

❏ Personal Knowledge   ❏ Credible Witness(es)   Type of I.D.: _____   Expiration Date: _____   Date of Birth: _____

| Type of Notarial Act: | ❏ Verbal Ceremony Performed | ❏ Other (Describe): | Fee: $ | |
| ❏ Oath/Affirmation | ❏ Acknowledgment | | Travel: $ | Right Thumbprint of Signer |

| Type of Document | Date of Document | Witness(es) Present | Other Signer(s) Present | |
| | | ❏ Yes ❏ No | ❏ Yes ❏ No | |

| Witness: Printed Name | Address/Phone | Signature of Witness | |

Comments; Additional Information:

If Notarization Failed or Refused, Give Reason:

❏ Insufficient ID   ❏ Signer Confused   ❏ Other (Explain in Comments Field)

91

| Printed Name of Signer: | Signer's Signature: | Time AM/PM: _____ |
| | | Date Notarized: _____ |

| Signer's Complete Address: | City | State | Zip | Phone |

| Identification by: | ❑ Identification Card | Issued By: _____ | I.D. # _____ |
| ❑ Personal Knowledge | ❑ Credible Witness(es) | Type of I.D.: _____ | Expiration Date: _____ | Date of Birth: _____ |

| Type of Notarial Act: | ❑ Verbal Ceremony Performed | ❑ Other (Describe): | Fee: $ | |
| ❑ Oath/Affirmation | ❑ Acknowledgment | | Travel: $ | |

| Type of Document | Date of Document | Witness(es) Present | Other Signer(s) Present | Right Thumbprint of Signer |
| | | ❑ Yes ❑ No | ❑ Yes ❑ No | |

| Witness: Printed Name | Address/Phone | Signature of Witness | |

| Comments; Additional Information: | If Notarization Failed or Refused, Give Reason: |
| | ❑ Insufficient ID ❑ Signer Confused ❑ Other (Explain in Comments Field) |

92

| Printed Name of Signer: | Signer's Signature: | Time AM/PM: _____ |
| | | Date Notarized: _____ |

| Signer's Complete Address: | City | State | Zip | Phone |

| Identification by: | ❑ Identification Card | Issued By: _____ | I.D. # _____ |
| ❑ Personal Knowledge | ❑ Credible Witness(es) | Type of I.D.: _____ | Expiration Date: _____ | Date of Birth: _____ |

| Type of Notarial Act: | ❑ Verbal Ceremony Performed | ❑ Other (Describe): | Fee: $ | |
| ❑ Oath/Affirmation | ❑ Acknowledgment | | Travel: $ | |

| Type of Document | Date of Document | Witness(es) Present | Other Signer(s) Present | Right Thumbprint of Signer |
| | | ❑ Yes ❑ No | ❑ Yes ❑ No | |

| Witness: Printed Name | Address/Phone | Signature of Witness | |

| Comments; Additional Information: | If Notarization Failed or Refused, Give Reason: |
| | ❑ Insufficient ID ❑ Signer Confused ❑ Other (Explain in Comments Field) |

93

| Printed Name of Signer: | Signer's Signature: | Time AM/PM: _____ |
| | | Date Notarized: _____ |

| Signer's Complete Address: | City | State | Zip | Phone |

| Identification by: | ❑ Identification Card | Issued By: _____ | I.D. # _____ |
| ❑ Personal Knowledge | ❑ Credible Witness(es) | Type of I.D.: _____ | Expiration Date: _____ | Date of Birth: _____ |

| Type of Notarial Act: | ❑ Verbal Ceremony Performed | ❑ Other (Describe): | Fee: $ | |
| ❑ Oath/Affirmation | ❑ Acknowledgment | | Travel: $ | |

| Type of Document | Date of Document | Witness(es) Present | Other Signer(s) Present | Right Thumbprint of Signer |
| | | ❑ Yes ❑ No | ❑ Yes ❑ No | |

| Witness: Printed Name | Address/Phone | Signature of Witness | |

| Comments; Additional Information: | If Notarization Failed or Refused, Give Reason: |
| | ❑ Insufficient ID ❑ Signer Confused ❑ Other (Explain in Comments Field) |

| Printed Name of Signer: | Signer's Signature: | Time AM/PM: _____ | **94** |
| | | Date Notarized: _____ | |

Signer's Complete Address:　　　　City　　　　State　Zip　　　Phone

Identification by:　　❑ Identification Card　　Issued By: _____　I.D. # _____

❑ Personal Knowledge　❑ Credible Witness(es)　Type of I.D.: _____　Expiration Date: _____　Date of Birth: _____

| Type of Notarial Act: | ❑ Verbal Ceremony Performed | ❑ Other (Describe): | Fee: $ | |
| ❑ Oath/Affirmation | ❑ Acknowledgment | | Travel: $ | |

Type of Document　　　Date of Document　Witness(es) Present　Other Signer(s) Present

❑ Yes ❑ No　　❑ Yes ❑ No

Right Thumbprint of Signer

Witness: Printed Name　　　Address/Phone　　　Signature of Witness

Comments; Additional Information:　　　If Notarization Failed or Refused, Give Reason:

❑ Insufficient ID　❑ Signer Confused　❑ Other (Explain in Comments Field)

| Printed Name of Signer: | Signer's Signature: | Time AM/PM: _____ | **95** |
| | | Date Notarized: _____ | |

Signer's Complete Address:　　　　City　　　　State　Zip　　　Phone

Identification by:　　❑ Identification Card　　Issued By: _____　I.D. # _____

❑ Personal Knowledge　❑ Credible Witness(es)　Type of I.D.: _____　Expiration Date: _____　Date of Birth: _____

| Type of Notarial Act: | ❑ Verbal Ceremony Performed | ❑ Other (Describe): | Fee: $ | |
| ❑ Oath/Affirmation | ❑ Acknowledgment | | Travel: $ | |

Type of Document　　　Date of Document　Witness(es) Present　Other Signer(s) Present

❑ Yes ❑ No　　❑ Yes ❑ No

Right Thumbprint of Signer

Witness: Printed Name　　　Address/Phone　　　Signature of Witness

Comments; Additional Information:　　　If Notarization Failed or Refused, Give Reason:

❑ Insufficient ID　❑ Signer Confused　❑ Other (Explain in Comments Field)

| Printed Name of Signer: | Signer's Signature: | Time AM/PM: _____ | **96** |
| | | Date Notarized: _____ | |

Signer's Complete Address:　　　　City　　　　State　Zip　　　Phone

Identification by:　　❑ Identification Card　　Issued By: _____　I.D. # _____

❑ Personal Knowledge　❑ Credible Witness(es)　Type of I.D.: _____　Expiration Date: _____　Date of Birth: _____

| Type of Notarial Act: | ❑ Verbal Ceremony Performed | ❑ Other (Describe): | Fee: $ | |
| ❑ Oath/Affirmation | ❑ Acknowledgment | | Travel: $ | |

Type of Document　　　Date of Document　Witness(es) Present　Other Signer(s) Present

❑ Yes ❑ No　　❑ Yes ❑ No

Right Thumbprint of Signer

Witness: Printed Name　　　Address/Phone　　　Signature of Witness

Comments; Additional Information:　　　If Notarization Failed or Refused, Give Reason:

❑ Insufficient ID　❑ Signer Confused　❑ Other (Explain in Comments Field)

97

| Printed Name of Signer: | Signer's Signature: | Time AM/PM: _____ |
| | | Date Notarized: _____ |

Signer's Complete Address: City   State   Zip   Phone

Identification by: ❏ Identification Card   Issued By: _____   I.D. #_____

❏ Personal Knowledge   ❏ Credible Witness(es)   Type of I.D.:_____   Expiration Date: _____   Date of Birth: _____

Type of Notarial Act: ❏ Verbal Ceremony Performed   ❏ Other (Describe):   Fee: $ _____

❏ Oath/Affirmation   ❏ Acknowledgment   Travel: $ _____

Type of Document   Date of Document   Witness(es) Present   Other Signer(s) Present

     ❏ Yes ❏ No   ❏ Yes ❏ No

Witness: Printed Name   Address/Phone   Signature of Witness

Right Thumbprint of Signer

Comments; Additional Information: If Notarization Failed or Refused, Give Reason:

❏ Insufficient ID   ❏ Signer Confused   ❏ Other (Explain in Comments Field)

98

| Printed Name of Signer: | Signer's Signature: | Time AM/PM: _____ |
| | | Date Notarized: _____ |

Signer's Complete Address: City   State   Zip   Phone

Identification by: ❏ Identification Card   Issued By: _____   I.D. #_____

❏ Personal Knowledge   ❏ Credible Witness(es)   Type of I.D.:_____   Expiration Date: _____   Date of Birth: _____

Type of Notarial Act: ❏ Verbal Ceremony Performed   ❏ Other (Describe):   Fee: $ _____

❏ Oath/Affirmation   ❏ Acknowledgment   Travel: $ _____

Type of Document   Date of Document   Witness(es) Present   Other Signer(s) Present

     ❏ Yes ❏ No   ❏ Yes ❏ No

Witness: Printed Name   Address/Phone   Signature of Witness

Right Thumbprint of Signer

Comments; Additional Information: If Notarization Failed or Refused, Give Reason:

❏ Insufficient ID   ❏ Signer Confused   ❏ Other (Explain in Comments Field)

99

| Printed Name of Signer: | Signer's Signature: | Time AM/PM: _____ |
| | | Date Notarized: _____ |

Signer's Complete Address: City   State   Zip   Phone

Identification by: ❏ Identification Card   Issued By: _____   I.D. #_____

❏ Personal Knowledge   ❏ Credible Witness(es)   Type of I.D.:_____   Expiration Date: _____   Date of Birth: _____

Type of Notarial Act: ❏ Verbal Ceremony Performed   ❏ Other (Describe):   Fee: $ _____

❏ Oath/Affirmation   ❏ Acknowledgment   Travel: $ _____

Type of Document   Date of Document   Witness(es) Present   Other Signer(s) Present

     ❏ Yes ❏ No   ❏ Yes ❏ No

Witness: Printed Name   Address/Phone   Signature of Witness

Right Thumbprint of Signer

Comments; Additional Information: If Notarization Failed or Refused, Give Reason:

❏ Insufficient ID   ❏ Signer Confused   ❏ Other (Explain in Comments Field)

100

| Printed Name of Signer: | Signer's Signature: | Time AM/PM: _____ |
| | | Date Notarized: _____ |

Signer's Complete Address: City   State   Zip   Phone

Identification by: ❏ Identification Card   Issued By: _____   I.D. # _____

❏ Personal Knowledge   ❏ Credible Witness(es)   Type of I.D.: _____   Expiration Date: _____   Date of Birth: _____

Type of Notarial Act: ❏ Verbal Ceremony Performed   ❏ Other (Describe):   Fee: $ _____

❏ Oath/Affirmation   ❏ Acknowledgment   Travel: $ _____

Type of Document   Date of Document   Witness(es) Present ❏ Yes ❏ No   Other Signer(s) Present ❏ Yes ❏ No

Witness: Printed Name   Address/Phone   Signature of Witness

Right Thumbprint of Signer

Comments; Additional Information:

If Notarization Failed or Refused, Give Reason:
❏ Insufficient ID   ❏ Signer Confused   ❏ Other (Explain in Comments Field)

101

| Printed Name of Signer: | Signer's Signature: | Time AM/PM: _____ |
| | | Date Notarized: _____ |

Signer's Complete Address: City   State   Zip   Phone

Identification by: ❏ Identification Card   Issued By: _____   I.D. # _____

❏ Personal Knowledge   ❏ Credible Witness(es)   Type of I.D.: _____   Expiration Date: _____   Date of Birth: _____

Type of Notarial Act: ❏ Verbal Ceremony Performed   ❏ Other (Describe):   Fee: $ _____

❏ Oath/Affirmation   ❏ Acknowledgment   Travel: $ _____

Type of Document   Date of Document   Witness(es) Present ❏ Yes ❏ No   Other Signer(s) Present ❏ Yes ❏ No

Witness: Printed Name   Address/Phone   Signature of Witness

Right Thumbprint of Signer

Comments; Additional Information:

If Notarization Failed or Refused, Give Reason:
❏ Insufficient ID   ❏ Signer Confused   ❏ Other (Explain in Comments Field)

102

| Printed Name of Signer: | Signer's Signature: | Time AM/PM: _____ |
| | | Date Notarized: _____ |

Signer's Complete Address: City   State   Zip   Phone

Identification by: ❏ Identification Card   Issued By: _____   I.D. # _____

❏ Personal Knowledge   ❏ Credible Witness(es)   Type of I.D.: _____   Expiration Date: _____   Date of Birth: _____

Type of Notarial Act: ❏ Verbal Ceremony Performed   ❏ Other (Describe):   Fee: $ _____

❏ Oath/Affirmation   ❏ Acknowledgment   Travel: $ _____

Type of Document   Date of Document   Witness(es) Present ❏ Yes ❏ No   Other Signer(s) Present ❏ Yes ❏ No

Witness: Printed Name   Address/Phone   Signature of Witness

Right Thumbprint of Signer

Comments; Additional Information:

If Notarization Failed or Refused, Give Reason:
❏ Insufficient ID   ❏ Signer Confused   ❏ Other (Explain in Comments Field)

103

| Printed Name of Signer: | Signer's Signature: | Time AM/PM: _____ |
| | | Date Notarized: _____ |

Signer's Complete Address: City State Zip Phone

Identification by: ❑ Identification Card Issued By: _____ I.D. #_____

❑ Personal Knowledge ❑ Credible Witness(es) Type of I.D.:_____ Expiration Date: _____ Date of Birth: _____

Type of Notarial Act: ❑ Verbal Ceremony Performed ❑ Other (Describe): Fee: $
❑ Oath/Affirmation ❑ Acknowledgment Travel: $

Type of Document Date of Document Witness(es) Present Other Signer(s) Present
❑ Yes ❑ No ❑ Yes ❑ No

Right Thumbprint of Signer

Witness: Printed Name Address/Phone Signature of Witness

Comments; Additional Information: If Notarization Failed or Refused, Give Reason:
❑ Insufficient ID ❑ Signer Confused ❑ Other (Explain in Comments Field)

104

| Printed Name of Signer: | Signer's Signature: | Time AM/PM: _____ |
| | | Date Notarized: _____ |

Signer's Complete Address: City State Zip Phone

Identification by: ❑ Identification Card Issued By: _____ I.D. #_____

❑ Personal Knowledge ❑ Credible Witness(es) Type of I.D.:_____ Expiration Date: _____ Date of Birth: _____

Type of Notarial Act: ❑ Verbal Ceremony Performed ❑ Other (Describe): Fee: $
❑ Oath/Affirmation ❑ Acknowledgment Travel: $

Type of Document Date of Document Witness(es) Present Other Signer(s) Present
❑ Yes ❑ No ❑ Yes ❑ No

Right Thumbprint of Signer

Witness: Printed Name Address/Phone Signature of Witness

Comments; Additional Information: If Notarization Failed or Refused, Give Reason:
❑ Insufficient ID ❑ Signer Confused ❑ Other (Explain in Comments Field)

105

| Printed Name of Signer: | Signer's Signature: | Time AM/PM: _____ |
| | | Date Notarized: _____ |

Signer's Complete Address: City State Zip Phone

Identification by: ❑ Identification Card Issued By: _____ I.D. #_____

❑ Personal Knowledge ❑ Credible Witness(es) Type of I.D.:_____ Expiration Date: _____ Date of Birth: _____

Type of Notarial Act: ❑ Verbal Ceremony Performed ❑ Other (Describe): Fee: $
❑ Oath/Affirmation ❑ Acknowledgment Travel: $

Type of Document Date of Document Witness(es) Present Other Signer(s) Present
❑ Yes ❑ No ❑ Yes ❑ No

Right Thumbprint of Signer

Witness: Printed Name Address/Phone Signature of Witness

Comments; Additional Information: If Notarization Failed or Refused, Give Reason:
❑ Insufficient ID ❑ Signer Confused ❑ Other (Explain in Comments Field)

106

| Printed Name of Signer: | Signer's Signature: | Time AM/PM: _____ |
| | | Date Notarized: _____ |

Signer's Complete Address: City   State   Zip   Phone

Identification by: ❏ Identification Card   Issued By: _____   I.D. # _____

❏ Personal Knowledge   ❏ Credible Witness(es)   Type of I.D.: _____   Expiration Date: _____   Date of Birth: _____

Type of Notarial Act: ❏ Verbal Ceremony Performed   ❏ Other (Describe):   Fee: $

❏ Oath/Affirmation   ❏ Acknowledgment   Travel: $

Type of Document   Date of Document   Witness(es) Present   Other Signer(s) Present

     ❏ Yes ❏ No   ❏ Yes ❏ No

Witness: Printed Name   Address/Phone   Signature of Witness

Right Thumbprint of Signer

Comments; Additional Information: If Notarization Failed or Refused, Give Reason:

❏ Insufficient ID   ❏ Signer Confused   ❏ Other (Explain in Comments Field)

107

| Printed Name of Signer: | Signer's Signature: | Time AM/PM: _____ |
| | | Date Notarized: _____ |

Signer's Complete Address: City   State   Zip   Phone

Identification by: ❏ Identification Card   Issued By: _____   I.D. # _____

❏ Personal Knowledge   ❏ Credible Witness(es)   Type of I.D.: _____   Expiration Date: _____   Date of Birth: _____

Type of Notarial Act: ❏ Verbal Ceremony Performed   ❏ Other (Describe):   Fee: $

❏ Oath/Affirmation   ❏ Acknowledgment   Travel: $

Type of Document   Date of Document   Witness(es) Present   Other Signer(s) Present

     ❏ Yes ❏ No   ❏ Yes ❏ No

Witness: Printed Name   Address/Phone   Signature of Witness

Right Thumbprint of Signer

Comments; Additional Information: If Notarization Failed or Refused, Give Reason:

❏ Insufficient ID   ❏ Signer Confused   ❏ Other (Explain in Comments Field)

108

| Printed Name of Signer: | Signer's Signature: | Time AM/PM: _____ |
| | | Date Notarized: _____ |

Signer's Complete Address: City   State   Zip   Phone

Identification by: ❏ Identification Card   Issued By: _____   I.D. # _____

❏ Personal Knowledge   ❏ Credible Witness(es)   Type of I.D.: _____   Expiration Date: _____   Date of Birth: _____

Type of Notarial Act: ❏ Verbal Ceremony Performed   ❏ Other (Describe):   Fee: $

❏ Oath/Affirmation   ❏ Acknowledgment   Travel: $

Type of Document   Date of Document   Witness(es) Present   Other Signer(s) Present

     ❏ Yes ❏ No   ❏ Yes ❏ No

Witness: Printed Name   Address/Phone   Signature of Witness

Right Thumbprint of Signer

Comments; Additional Information: If Notarization Failed or Refused, Give Reason:

❏ Insufficient ID   ❏ Signer Confused   ❏ Other (Explain in Comments Field)

109

Printed Name of Signer:	Signer's Signature:	Time AM/PM: _____ Date Notarized: _____

Signer's Complete Address: City   State   Zip   Phone

Identification by:

❑ Personal Knowledge   ❑ Identification Card   Issued By: _____   I.D. # _____

❑ Credible Witness(es)   Type of I.D.: _____   Expiration Date: _____   Date of Birth: _____

Type of Notarial Act: ❑ Verbal Ceremony Performed   ❑ Other (Describe):   Fee: $ _____

❑ Oath/Affirmation   ❑ Acknowledgment   Travel: $ _____

Type of Document   Date of Document   Witness(es) Present   Other Signer(s) Present

   ❑ Yes ❑ No   ❑ Yes ❑ No

Witness: Printed Name   Address/Phone   Signature of Witness

Right Thumbprint of Signer

Comments; Additional Information: If Notarization Failed or Refused, Give Reason:

❑ Insufficient ID   ❑ Signer Confused   ❑ Other (Explain in Comments Field)

110

Printed Name of Signer:	Signer's Signature:	Time AM/PM: _____ Date Notarized: _____

Signer's Complete Address: City   State   Zip   Phone

Identification by:

❑ Personal Knowledge   ❑ Identification Card   Issued By: _____   I.D. # _____

❑ Credible Witness(es)   Type of I.D.: _____   Expiration Date: _____   Date of Birth: _____

Type of Notarial Act: ❑ Verbal Ceremony Performed   ❑ Other (Describe):   Fee: $ _____

❑ Oath/Affirmation   ❑ Acknowledgment   Travel: $ _____

Type of Document   Date of Document   Witness(es) Present   Other Signer(s) Present

   ❑ Yes ❑ No   ❑ Yes ❑ No

Witness: Printed Name   Address/Phone   Signature of Witness

Right Thumbprint of Signer

Comments; Additional Information: If Notarization Failed or Refused, Give Reason:

❑ Insufficient ID   ❑ Signer Confused   ❑ Other (Explain in Comments Field)

111

Printed Name of Signer:	Signer's Signature:	Time AM/PM: _____ Date Notarized: _____

Signer's Complete Address: City   State   Zip   Phone

Identification by:

❑ Personal Knowledge   ❑ Identification Card   Issued By: _____   I.D. # _____

❑ Credible Witness(es)   Type of I.D.: _____   Expiration Date: _____   Date of Birth: _____

Type of Notarial Act: ❑ Verbal Ceremony Performed   ❑ Other (Describe):   Fee: $ _____

❑ Oath/Affirmation   ❑ Acknowledgment   Travel: $ _____

Type of Document   Date of Document   Witness(es) Present   Other Signer(s) Present

   ❑ Yes ❑ No   ❑ Yes ❑ No

Witness: Printed Name   Address/Phone   Signature of Witness

Right Thumbprint of Signer

Comments; Additional Information: If Notarization Failed or Refused, Give Reason:

❑ Insufficient ID   ❑ Signer Confused   ❑ Other (Explain in Comments Field)

112

Printed Name of Signer:

Signer's Signature:

Time AM/PM: _____
Date Notarized: _____

Signer's Complete Address: City State Zip Phone

Identification by: ❑ Identification Card Issued By: _____ I.D. # _____

❑ Personal Knowledge ❑ Credible Witness(es) Type of I.D.: _____ Expiration Date: _____ Date of Birth: _____

Type of Notarial Act: ❑ Verbal Ceremony Performed ❑ Other (Describe): Fee: $

❑ Oath/Affirmation ❑ Acknowledgment Travel: $

Type of Document Date of Document Witness(es) Present Other Signer(s) Present

❑ Yes ❑ No ❑ Yes ❑ No

Witness: Printed Name Address/Phone Signature of Witness

Right Thumbprint of Signer

Comments; Additional Information:

If Notarization Failed or Refused, Give Reason:

❑ Insufficient ID ❑ Signer Confused ❑ Other (Explain in Comments Field)

113

Printed Name of Signer:

Signer's Signature:

Time AM/PM: _____
Date Notarized: _____

Signer's Complete Address: City State Zip Phone

Identification by: ❑ Identification Card Issued By: _____ I.D. # _____

❑ Personal Knowledge ❑ Credible Witness(es) Type of I.D.: _____ Expiration Date: _____ Date of Birth: _____

Type of Notarial Act: ❑ Verbal Ceremony Performed ❑ Other (Describe): Fee: $

❑ Oath/Affirmation ❑ Acknowledgment Travel: $

Type of Document Date of Document Witness(es) Present Other Signer(s) Present

❑ Yes ❑ No ❑ Yes ❑ No

Witness: Printed Name Address/Phone Signature of Witness

Right Thumbprint of Signer

Comments; Additional Information:

If Notarization Failed or Refused, Give Reason:

❑ Insufficient ID ❑ Signer Confused ❑ Other (Explain in Comments Field)

114

Printed Name of Signer:

Signer's Signature:

Time AM/PM: _____
Date Notarized: _____

Signer's Complete Address: City State Zip Phone

Identification by: ❑ Identification Card Issued By: _____ I.D. # _____

❑ Personal Knowledge ❑ Credible Witness(es) Type of I.D.: _____ Expiration Date: _____ Date of Birth: _____

Type of Notarial Act: ❑ Verbal Ceremony Performed ❑ Other (Describe): Fee: $

❑ Oath/Affirmation ❑ Acknowledgment Travel: $

Type of Document Date of Document Witness(es) Present Other Signer(s) Present

❑ Yes ❑ No ❑ Yes ❑ No

Witness: Printed Name Address/Phone Signature of Witness

Right Thumbprint of Signer

Comments; Additional Information:

If Notarization Failed or Refused, Give Reason:

❑ Insufficient ID ❑ Signer Confused ❑ Other (Explain in Comments Field)

115

Printed Name of Signer:	Signer's Signature:	Time AM/PM: _____
		Date Notarized: _____

Signer's Complete Address: City State Zip Phone

Identification by: ❏ Identification Card Issued By: _____ I.D. # _____

❏ Personal Knowledge ❏ Credible Witness(es) Type of I.D.: _____ Expiration Date: _____ Date of Birth: _____

Type of Notarial Act: ❏ Verbal Ceremony Performed ❏ Other (Describe): Fee: $
❏ Oath/Affirmation ❏ Acknowledgment Travel: $

Type of Document Date of Document Witness(es) Present Other Signer(s) Present
❏ Yes ❏ No ❏ Yes ❏ No

Witness: Printed Name Address/Phone Signature of Witness

Right Thumbprint of Signer

Comments; Additional Information: If Notarization Failed or Refused, Give Reason:
❏ Insufficient ID ❏ Signer Confused ❏ Other (Explain in Comments Field)

116

Printed Name of Signer:	Signer's Signature:	Time AM/PM: _____
		Date Notarized: _____

Signer's Complete Address: City State Zip Phone

Identification by: ❏ Identification Card Issued By: _____ I.D. # _____

❏ Personal Knowledge ❏ Credible Witness(es) Type of I.D.: _____ Expiration Date: _____ Date of Birth: _____

Type of Notarial Act: ❏ Verbal Ceremony Performed ❏ Other (Describe): Fee: $
❏ Oath/Affirmation ❏ Acknowledgment Travel: $

Type of Document Date of Document Witness(es) Present Other Signer(s) Present
❏ Yes ❏ No ❏ Yes ❏ No

Witness: Printed Name Address/Phone Signature of Witness

Right Thumbprint of Signer

Comments; Additional Information: If Notarization Failed or Refused, Give Reason:
❏ Insufficient ID ❏ Signer Confused ❏ Other (Explain in Comments Field)

117

Printed Name of Signer:	Signer's Signature:	Time AM/PM: _____
		Date Notarized: _____

Signer's Complete Address: City State Zip Phone

Identification by: ❏ Identification Card Issued By: _____ I.D. # _____

❏ Personal Knowledge ❏ Credible Witness(es) Type of I.D.: _____ Expiration Date: _____ Date of Birth: _____

Type of Notarial Act: ❏ Verbal Ceremony Performed ❏ Other (Describe): Fee: $
❏ Oath/Affirmation ❏ Acknowledgment Travel: $

Type of Document Date of Document Witness(es) Present Other Signer(s) Present
❏ Yes ❏ No ❏ Yes ❏ No

Witness: Printed Name Address/Phone Signature of Witness

Right Thumbprint of Signer

Comments; Additional Information: If Notarization Failed or Refused, Give Reason:
❏ Insufficient ID ❏ Signer Confused ❏ Other (Explain in Comments Field)

118

Printed Name of Signer:	Signer's Signature:	Time AM/PM: _____
		Date Notarized: _____

Signer's Complete Address: City   State   Zip   Phone

Identification by: ❏ Identification Card   Issued By: _____   I.D. # _____

❏ Personal Knowledge   ❏ Credible Witness(es)   Type of I.D.: _____   Expiration Date: _____   Date of Birth: _____

Type of Notarial Act: ❏ Verbal Ceremony Performed   ❏ Other (Describe):   Fee: $

❏ Oath/Affirmation   ❏ Acknowledgment   Travel: $

Type of Document   Date of Document   Witness(es) Present   Other Signer(s) Present

     ❏ Yes ❏ No   ❏ Yes ❏ No

Witness: Printed Name   Address/Phone   Signature of Witness

Right Thumbprint of Signer

Comments; Additional Information: If Notarization Failed or Refused, Give Reason:

❏ Insufficient ID   ❏ Signer Confused   ❏ Other (Explain in Comments Field)

119

Printed Name of Signer:	Signer's Signature:	Time AM/PM: _____
		Date Notarized: _____

Signer's Complete Address: City   State   Zip   Phone

Identification by: ❏ Identification Card   Issued By: _____   I.D. # _____

❏ Personal Knowledge   ❏ Credible Witness(es)   Type of I.D.: _____   Expiration Date: _____   Date of Birth: _____

Type of Notarial Act: ❏ Verbal Ceremony Performed   ❏ Other (Describe):   Fee: $

❏ Oath/Affirmation   ❏ Acknowledgment   Travel: $

Type of Document   Date of Document   Witness(es) Present   Other Signer(s) Present

     ❏ Yes ❏ No   ❏ Yes ❏ No

Witness: Printed Name   Address/Phone   Signature of Witness

Right Thumbprint of Signer

Comments; Additional Information: If Notarization Failed or Refused, Give Reason:

❏ Insufficient ID   ❏ Signer Confused   ❏ Other (Explain in Comments Field)

120

Printed Name of Signer:	Signer's Signature:	Time AM/PM: _____
		Date Notarized: _____

Signer's Complete Address: City   State   Zip   Phone

Identification by: ❏ Identification Card   Issued By: _____   I.D. # _____

❏ Personal Knowledge   ❏ Credible Witness(es)   Type of I.D.: _____   Expiration Date: _____   Date of Birth: _____

Type of Notarial Act: ❏ Verbal Ceremony Performed   ❏ Other (Describe):   Fee: $

❏ Oath/Affirmation   ❏ Acknowledgment   Travel: $

Type of Document   Date of Document   Witness(es) Present   Other Signer(s) Present

     ❏ Yes ❏ No   ❏ Yes ❏ No

Witness: Printed Name   Address/Phone   Signature of Witness

Right Thumbprint of Signer

Comments; Additional Information: If Notarization Failed or Refused, Give Reason:

❏ Insufficient ID   ❏ Signer Confused   ❏ Other (Explain in Comments Field)

121

Printed Name of Signer:

Signer's Signature:

Time AM/PM: _____

Date Notarized: _____

Signer's Complete Address:

City   State   Zip   Phone

Identification by:

❑ Identification Card   Issued By: _____   I.D. # _____

❑ Personal Knowledge   ❑ Credible Witness(es)   Type of I.D.: _____   Expiration Date: _____   Date of Birth: _____

Type of Notarial Act: ❑ Verbal Ceremony Performed   ❑ Other (Describe):   Fee: $

❑ Oath/Affirmation   ❑ Acknowledgment   Travel: $

Type of Document   Date of Document   Witness(es) Present   Other Signer(s) Present

❑ Yes ❑ No   ❑ Yes ❑ No

Right Thumbprint of Signer

Witness: Printed Name   Address/Phone   Signature of Witness

Comments; Additional Information: If Notarization Failed or Refused, Give Reason:

❑ Insufficient ID   ❑ Signer Confused   ❑ Other (Explain in Comments Field)

122

Printed Name of Signer:

Signer's Signature:

Time AM/PM: _____

Date Notarized: _____

Signer's Complete Address:

City   State   Zip   Phone

Identification by:

❑ Identification Card   Issued By: _____   I.D. # _____

❑ Personal Knowledge   ❑ Credible Witness(es)   Type of I.D.: _____   Expiration Date: _____   Date of Birth: _____

Type of Notarial Act: ❑ Verbal Ceremony Performed   ❑ Other (Describe):   Fee: $

❑ Oath/Affirmation   ❑ Acknowledgment   Travel: $

Type of Document   Date of Document   Witness(es) Present   Other Signer(s) Present

❑ Yes ❑ No   ❑ Yes ❑ No

Right Thumbprint of Signer

Witness: Printed Name   Address/Phone   Signature of Witness

Comments; Additional Information: If Notarization Failed or Refused, Give Reason:

❑ Insufficient ID   ❑ Signer Confused   ❑ Other (Explain in Comments Field)

123

Printed Name of Signer:

Signer's Signature:

Time AM/PM: _____

Date Notarized: _____

Signer's Complete Address:

City   State   Zip   Phone

Identification by:

❑ Identification Card   Issued By: _____   I.D. # _____

❑ Personal Knowledge   ❑ Credible Witness(es)   Type of I.D.: _____   Expiration Date: _____   Date of Birth: _____

Type of Notarial Act: ❑ Verbal Ceremony Performed   ❑ Other (Describe):   Fee: $

❑ Oath/Affirmation   ❑ Acknowledgment   Travel: $

Type of Document   Date of Document   Witness(es) Present   Other Signer(s) Present

❑ Yes ❑ No   ❑ Yes ❑ No

Right Thumbprint of Signer

Witness: Printed Name   Address/Phone   Signature of Witness

Comments; Additional Information: If Notarization Failed or Refused, Give Reason:

❑ Insufficient ID   ❑ Signer Confused   ❑ Other (Explain in Comments Field)

124

Printed Name of Signer:

Signer's Signature:

Time AM/PM: _____

Date Notarized: _____

Signer's Complete Address:　　　City　　　State　　Zip　　Phone

Identification by:　　❑ Identification Card　　Issued By: _____　I.D. # _____

❑ Personal Knowledge　❑ Credible Witness(es)　Type of I.D.: _____　Expiration Date: _____　Date of Birth: _____

Type of Notarial Act:　❑ Verbal Ceremony Performed　❑ Other (Describe):　　Fee: $

❑ Oath/Affirmation　❑ Acknowledgment　　　Travel: $

Right Thumbprint of Signer

Type of Document　　Date of Document　Witness(es) Present　Other Signer(s) Present

❑ Yes ❑ No　❑ Yes ❑ No

Witness: Printed Name　　Address/Phone　　Signature of Witness

Comments; Additional Information:　　If Notarization Failed or Refused, Give Reason:

❑ Insufficient ID　❑ Signer Confused　❑ Other (Explain in Comments Field)

125

Printed Name of Signer:

Signer's Signature:

Time AM/PM: _____

Date Notarized: _____

Signer's Complete Address:　　　City　　　State　　Zip　　Phone

Identification by:　　❑ Identification Card　　Issued By: _____　I.D. # _____

❑ Personal Knowledge　❑ Credible Witness(es)　Type of I.D.: _____　Expiration Date: _____　Date of Birth: _____

Type of Notarial Act:　❑ Verbal Ceremony Performed　❑ Other (Describe):　　Fee: $

❑ Oath/Affirmation　❑ Acknowledgment　　　Travel: $

Right Thumbprint of Signer

Type of Document　　Date of Document　Witness(es) Present　Other Signer(s) Present

❑ Yes ❑ No　❑ Yes ❑ No

Witness: Printed Name　　Address/Phone　　Signature of Witness

Comments; Additional Information:　　If Notarization Failed or Refused, Give Reason:

❑ Insufficient ID　❑ Signer Confused　❑ Other (Explain in Comments Field)

126

Printed Name of Signer:

Signer's Signature:

Time AM/PM: _____

Date Notarized: _____

Signer's Complete Address:　　　City　　　State　　Zip　　Phone

Identification by:　　❑ Identification Card　　Issued By: _____　I.D. # _____

❑ Personal Knowledge　❑ Credible Witness(es)　Type of I.D.: _____　Expiration Date: _____　Date of Birth: _____

Type of Notarial Act:　❑ Verbal Ceremony Performed　❑ Other (Describe):　　Fee: $

❑ Oath/Affirmation　❑ Acknowledgment　　　Travel: $

Right Thumbprint of Signer

Type of Document　　Date of Document　Witness(es) Present　Other Signer(s) Present

❑ Yes ❑ No　❑ Yes ❑ No

Witness: Printed Name　　Address/Phone　　Signature of Witness

Comments; Additional Information:　　If Notarization Failed or Refused, Give Reason:

❑ Insufficient ID　❑ Signer Confused　❑ Other (Explain in Comments Field)

127

| Printed Name of Signer: | Signer's Signature: | Time AM/PM: _____ |
| | | Date Notarized: _____ |

Signer's Complete Address: City State Zip Phone

Identification by: ❏ Identification Card Issued By: _____ I.D. # _____

❏ Personal Knowledge ❏ Credible Witness(es) Type of I.D.: _____ Expiration Date: _____ Date of Birth: _____

Type of Notarial Act: ❏ Verbal Ceremony Performed ❏ Other (Describe): Fee: $ _____ Travel: $ _____

❏ Oath/Affirmation ❏ Acknowledgment

Type of Document Date of Document Witness(es) Present ❏ Yes ❏ No Other Signer(s) Present ❏ Yes ❏ No

Witness: Printed Name Address/Phone Signature of Witness

Right Thumbprint of Signer

Comments; Additional Information: If Notarization Failed or Refused, Give Reason:
❏ Insufficient ID ❏ Signer Confused ❏ Other (Explain in Comments Field)

128

| Printed Name of Signer: | Signer's Signature: | Time AM/PM: _____ |
| | | Date Notarized: _____ |

Signer's Complete Address: City State Zip Phone

Identification by: ❏ Identification Card Issued By: _____ I.D. # _____

❏ Personal Knowledge ❏ Credible Witness(es) Type of I.D.: _____ Expiration Date: _____ Date of Birth: _____

Type of Notarial Act: ❏ Verbal Ceremony Performed ❏ Other (Describe): Fee: $ _____ Travel: $ _____

❏ Oath/Affirmation ❏ Acknowledgment

Type of Document Date of Document Witness(es) Present ❏ Yes ❏ No Other Signer(s) Present ❏ Yes ❏ No

Witness: Printed Name Address/Phone Signature of Witness

Right Thumbprint of Signer

Comments; Additional Information: If Notarization Failed or Refused, Give Reason:
❏ Insufficient ID ❏ Signer Confused ❏ Other (Explain in Comments Field)

129

| Printed Name of Signer: | Signer's Signature: | Time AM/PM: _____ |
| | | Date Notarized: _____ |

Signer's Complete Address: City State Zip Phone

Identification by: ❏ Identification Card Issued By: _____ I.D. # _____

❏ Personal Knowledge ❏ Credible Witness(es) Type of I.D.: _____ Expiration Date: _____ Date of Birth: _____

Type of Notarial Act: ❏ Verbal Ceremony Performed ❏ Other (Describe): Fee: $ _____ Travel: $ _____

❏ Oath/Affirmation ❏ Acknowledgment

Type of Document Date of Document Witness(es) Present ❏ Yes ❏ No Other Signer(s) Present ❏ Yes ❏ No

Witness: Printed Name Address/Phone Signature of Witness

Right Thumbprint of Signer

Comments; Additional Information: If Notarization Failed or Refused, Give Reason:
❏ Insufficient ID ❏ Signer Confused ❏ Other (Explain in Comments Field)

130

| Printed Name of Signer: | Signer's Signature: | Time AM/PM: _____ |
| | | Date Notarized: _____ |

Signer's Complete Address: City   State   Zip   Phone

Identification by: ❏ Identification Card   Issued By: _____   I.D. # _____

❏ Personal Knowledge   ❏ Credible Witness(es)   Type of I.D.: _____   Expiration Date: _____   Date of Birth: _____

Type of Notarial Act: ❏ Verbal Ceremony Performed   ❏ Other (Describe):   Fee: $

❏ Oath/Affirmation   ❏ Acknowledgment   Travel: $

Type of Document   Date of Document   Witness(es) Present   Other Signer(s) Present

      ❏ Yes ❏ No   ❏ Yes ❏ No

Witness: Printed Name   Address/Phone   Signature of Witness

Right Thumbprint of Signer

Comments; Additional Information: If Notarization Failed or Refused, Give Reason:

❏ Insufficient ID   ❏ Signer Confused   ❏ Other (Explain in Comments Field)

131

| Printed Name of Signer: | Signer's Signature: | Time AM/PM: _____ |
| | | Date Notarized: _____ |

Signer's Complete Address: City   State   Zip   Phone

Identification by: ❏ Identification Card   Issued By: _____   I.D. # _____

❏ Personal Knowledge   ❏ Credible Witness(es)   Type of I.D.: _____   Expiration Date: _____   Date of Birth: _____

Type of Notarial Act: ❏ Verbal Ceremony Performed   ❏ Other (Describe):   Fee: $

❏ Oath/Affirmation   ❏ Acknowledgment   Travel: $

Type of Document   Date of Document   Witness(es) Present   Other Signer(s) Present

      ❏ Yes ❏ No   ❏ Yes ❏ No

Witness: Printed Name   Address/Phone   Signature of Witness

Right Thumbprint of Signer

Comments; Additional Information: If Notarization Failed or Refused, Give Reason:

❏ Insufficient ID   ❏ Signer Confused   ❏ Other (Explain in Comments Field)

132

| Printed Name of Signer: | Signer's Signature: | Time AM/PM: _____ |
| | | Date Notarized: _____ |

Signer's Complete Address: City   State   Zip   Phone

Identification by: ❏ Identification Card   Issued By: _____   I.D. # _____

❏ Personal Knowledge   ❏ Credible Witness(es)   Type of I.D.: _____   Expiration Date: _____   Date of Birth: _____

Type of Notarial Act: ❏ Verbal Ceremony Performed   ❏ Other (Describe):   Fee: $

❏ Oath/Affirmation   ❏ Acknowledgment   Travel: $

Type of Document   Date of Document   Witness(es) Present   Other Signer(s) Present

      ❏ Yes ❏ No   ❏ Yes ❏ No

Witness: Printed Name   Address/Phone   Signature of Witness

Right Thumbprint of Signer

Comments; Additional Information: If Notarization Failed or Refused, Give Reason:

❏ Insufficient ID   ❏ Signer Confused   ❏ Other (Explain in Comments Field)

133

| Printed Name of Signer: | Signer's Signature: | Time AM/PM: _____ |
| | | Date Notarized: _____ |

Signer's Complete Address: City   State   Zip   Phone

Identification by: ❑ Identification Card   Issued By: _____   I.D. # _____

❑ Personal Knowledge   ❑ Credible Witness(es)   Type of I.D.: _____   Expiration Date: _____   Date of Birth: _____

Type of Notarial Act: ❑ Verbal Ceremony Performed   ❑ Other (Describe):   Fee: $

❑ Oath/Affirmation   ❑ Acknowledgment   Travel: $

Type of Document   Date of Document   Witness(es) Present   Other Signer(s) Present

    ❑ Yes ❑ No   ❑ Yes ❑ No

Witness: Printed Name   Address/Phone   Signature of Witness

Right Thumbprint of Signer

Comments; Additional Information: If Notarization Failed or Refused, Give Reason:

❑ Insufficient ID   ❑ Signer Confused   ❑ Other (Explain in Comments Field)

134

| Printed Name of Signer: | Signer's Signature: | Time AM/PM: _____ |
| | | Date Notarized: _____ |

Signer's Complete Address: City   State   Zip   Phone

Identification by: ❑ Identification Card   Issued By: _____   I.D. # _____

❑ Personal Knowledge   ❑ Credible Witness(es)   Type of I.D.: _____   Expiration Date: _____   Date of Birth: _____

Type of Notarial Act: ❑ Verbal Ceremony Performed   ❑ Other (Describe):   Fee: $

❑ Oath/Affirmation   ❑ Acknowledgment   Travel: $

Type of Document   Date of Document   Witness(es) Present   Other Signer(s) Present

    ❑ Yes ❑ No   ❑ Yes ❑ No

Witness: Printed Name   Address/Phone   Signature of Witness

Right Thumbprint of Signer

Comments; Additional Information: If Notarization Failed or Refused, Give Reason:

❑ Insufficient ID   ❑ Signer Confused   ❑ Other (Explain in Comments Field)

135

| Printed Name of Signer: | Signer's Signature: | Time AM/PM: _____ |
| | | Date Notarized: _____ |

Signer's Complete Address: City   State   Zip   Phone

Identification by: ❑ Identification Card   Issued By: _____   I.D. # _____

❑ Personal Knowledge   ❑ Credible Witness(es)   Type of I.D.: _____   Expiration Date: _____   Date of Birth: _____

Type of Notarial Act: ❑ Verbal Ceremony Performed   ❑ Other (Describe):   Fee: $

❑ Oath/Affirmation   ❑ Acknowledgment   Travel: $

Type of Document   Date of Document   Witness(es) Present   Other Signer(s) Present

    ❑ Yes ❑ No   ❑ Yes ❑ No

Witness: Printed Name   Address/Phone   Signature of Witness

Right Thumbprint of Signer

Comments; Additional Information: If Notarization Failed or Refused, Give Reason:

❑ Insufficient ID   ❑ Signer Confused   ❑ Other (Explain in Comments Field)

Printed Name of Signer: **Signer's Signature:**   Time AM/PM: _____   **136**

Date Notarized: _____

Signer's Complete Address: City   State   Zip   Phone

Identification by: ❏ Identification Card   Issued By: _____   I.D. # _____

❏ **Personal Knowledge**   ❏ Credible Witness(es)   Type of I.D.: _____   Expiration Date: _____   Date of Birth: _____

Type of Notarial Act: ❏ Verbal Ceremony Performed   ❏ Other (Describe):   Fee: $

❏ **Oath/Affirmation**   ❏ Acknowledgment   Travel: $

Type of Document   Date of Document   Witness(es) Present   Other Signer(s) Present

❏ Yes ❏ No   ❏ Yes ❏ No

Right Thumbprint of Signer

Witness: Printed Name   Address/Phone   Signature of Witness

Comments; Additional Information: If Notarization Failed or Refused, Give Reason:

❏ Insufficient ID   ❏ Signer Confused   ❏ Other (Explain in Comments Field)

Printed Name of Signer: **Signer's Signature:**   Time AM/PM: _____   **137**

Date Notarized: _____

Signer's Complete Address: City   State   Zip   Phone

Identification by: ❏ Identification Card   Issued By: _____   I.D. # _____

❏ **Personal Knowledge**   ❏ Credible Witness(es)   Type of I.D.: _____   Expiration Date: _____   Date of Birth: _____

Type of Notarial Act: ❏ Verbal Ceremony Performed   ❏ Other (Describe):   Fee: $

❏ **Oath/Affirmation**   ❏ Acknowledgment   Travel: $

Type of Document   Date of Document   Witness(es) Present   Other Signer(s) Present

❏ Yes ❏ No   ❏ Yes ❏ No

Right Thumbprint of Signer

Witness: Printed Name   Address/Phone   Signature of Witness

Comments; Additional Information: If Notarization Failed or Refused, Give Reason:

❏ Insufficient ID   ❏ Signer Confused   ❏ Other (Explain in Comments Field)

Printed Name of Signer: **Signer's Signature:**   Time AM/PM: _____   **138**

Date Notarized: _____

Signer's Complete Address: City   State   Zip   Phone

Identification by: ❏ Identification Card   Issued By: _____   I.D. # _____

❏ **Personal Knowledge**   ❏ Credible Witness(es)   Type of I.D.: _____   Expiration Date: _____   Date of Birth: _____

Type of Notarial Act: ❏ Verbal Ceremony Performed   ❏ Other (Describe):   Fee: $

❏ **Oath/Affirmation**   ❏ Acknowledgment   Travel: $

Type of Document   Date of Document   Witness(es) Present   Other Signer(s) Present

❏ Yes ❏ No   ❏ Yes ❏ No

Right Thumbprint of Signer

Witness: Printed Name   Address/Phone   Signature of Witness

Comments; Additional Information: If Notarization Failed or Refused, Give Reason:

❏ Insufficient ID   ❏ Signer Confused   ❏ Other (Explain in Comments Field)

139

Printed Name of Signer:

Signer's Signature:

Time AM/PM: _____
Date Notarized: _____

Signer's Complete Address: City   State   Zip   Phone

Identification by: ❑ Identification Card   Issued By: _____   I.D. # _____

❑ Personal Knowledge   ❑ Credible Witness(es)   Type of I.D.: _____   Expiration Date: _____   Date of Birth: _____

Type of Notarial Act: ❑ Verbal Ceremony Performed   ❑ Other (Describe):   Fee: $ Travel: $ Right Thumbprint of Signer

❑ Oath/Affirmation   ❑ Acknowledgment

Type of Document   Date of Document   Witness(es) Present ❑ Yes ❑ No   Other Signer(s) Present ❑ Yes ❑ No

Witness: Printed Name   Address/Phone   Signature of Witness

Comments; Additional Information: If Notarization Failed or Refused, Give Reason:
❑ Insufficient ID   ❑ Signer Confused   ❑ Other (Explain in Comments Field)

140

Printed Name of Signer:

Signer's Signature:

Time AM/PM: _____
Date Notarized: _____

Signer's Complete Address: City   State   Zip   Phone

Identification by: ❑ Identification Card   Issued By: _____   I.D. # _____

❑ Personal Knowledge   ❑ Credible Witness(es)   Type of I.D.: _____   Expiration Date: _____   Date of Birth: _____

Type of Notarial Act: ❑ Verbal Ceremony Performed   ❑ Other (Describe):   Fee: $ Travel: $ Right Thumbprint of Signer

❑ Oath/Affirmation   ❑ Acknowledgment

Type of Document   Date of Document   Witness(es) Present ❑ Yes ❑ No   Other Signer(s) Present ❑ Yes ❑ No

Witness: Printed Name   Address/Phone   Signature of Witness

Comments; Additional Information: If Notarization Failed or Refused, Give Reason:
❑ Insufficient ID   ❑ Signer Confused   ❑ Other (Explain in Comments Field)

141

Printed Name of Signer:

Signer's Signature:

Time AM/PM: _____
Date Notarized: _____

Signer's Complete Address: City   State   Zip   Phone

Identification by: ❑ Identification Card   Issued By: _____   I.D. # _____

❑ Personal Knowledge   ❑ Credible Witness(es)   Type of I.D.: _____   Expiration Date: _____   Date of Birth: _____

Type of Notarial Act: ❑ Verbal Ceremony Performed   ❑ Other (Describe):   Fee: $ Travel: $ Right Thumbprint of Signer

❑ Oath/Affirmation   ❑ Acknowledgment

Type of Document   Date of Document   Witness(es) Present ❑ Yes ❑ No   Other Signer(s) Present ❑ Yes ❑ No

Witness: Printed Name   Address/Phone   Signature of Witness

Comments; Additional Information: If Notarization Failed or Refused, Give Reason:
❑ Insufficient ID   ❑ Signer Confused   ❑ Other (Explain in Comments Field)

142

| Printed Name of Signer: | Signer's Signature: | Time AM/PM: _____ |
| | | Date Notarized: _____ |

Signer's Complete Address: City State Zip Phone

Identification by: ❑ Identification Card Issued By: _____ I.D. # _____

❑ Personal Knowledge ❑ Credible Witness(es) Type of I.D.: _____ Expiration Date: _____ Date of Birth: _____

| Type of Notarial Act: | ❑ Verbal Ceremony Performed | ❑ Other (Describe): | Fee: $ | |
| ❑ Oath/Affirmation | ❑ Acknowledgment | | Travel: $ | |

Type of Document Date of Document Witness(es) Present Other Signer(s) Present

❑ Yes ❑ No ❑ Yes ❑ No

Witness: Printed Name Address/Phone Signature of Witness

Right Thumbprint of Signer

Comments; Additional Information:

If Notarization Failed or Refused, Give Reason:

❑ Insufficient ID ❑ Signer Confused ❑ Other (Explain in Comments Field)

143

| Printed Name of Signer: | Signer's Signature: | Time AM/PM: _____ |
| | | Date Notarized: _____ |

Signer's Complete Address: City State Zip Phone

Identification by: ❑ Identification Card Issued By: _____ I.D. # _____

❑ Personal Knowledge ❑ Credible Witness(es) Type of I.D.: _____ Expiration Date: _____ Date of Birth: _____

| Type of Notarial Act: | ❑ Verbal Ceremony Performed | ❑ Other (Describe): | Fee: $ | |
| ❑ Oath/Affirmation | ❑ Acknowledgment | | Travel: $ | |

Type of Document Date of Document Witness(es) Present Other Signer(s) Present

❑ Yes ❑ No ❑ Yes ❑ No

Witness: Printed Name Address/Phone Signature of Witness

Right Thumbprint of Signer

Comments; Additional Information:

If Notarization Failed or Refused, Give Reason:

❑ Insufficient ID ❑ Signer Confused ❑ Other (Explain in Comments Field)

144

| Printed Name of Signer: | Signer's Signature: | Time AM/PM: _____ |
| | | Date Notarized: _____ |

Signer's Complete Address: City State Zip Phone

Identification by: ❑ Identification Card Issued By: _____ I.D. # _____

❑ Personal Knowledge ❑ Credible Witness(es) Type of I.D.: _____ Expiration Date: _____ Date of Birth: _____

| Type of Notarial Act: | ❑ Verbal Ceremony Performed | ❑ Other (Describe): | Fee: $ | |
| ❑ Oath/Affirmation | ❑ Acknowledgment | | Travel: $ | |

Type of Document Date of Document Witness(es) Present Other Signer(s) Present

❑ Yes ❑ No ❑ Yes ❑ No

Witness: Printed Name Address/Phone Signature of Witness

Right Thumbprint of Signer

Comments; Additional Information:

If Notarization Failed or Refused, Give Reason:

❑ Insufficient ID ❑ Signer Confused ❑ Other (Explain in Comments Field)

145

| Printed Name of Signer: | Signer's Signature: | Time AM/PM: _____ |
| | | Date Notarized: _____ |

| Signer's Complete Address: | City | State | Zip | Phone |

| Identification by: | ❏ Identification Card | Issued By: _____ | I.D. # _____ |
| ❏ Personal Knowledge | ❏ Credible Witness(es) | Type of I.D.: _____ | Expiration Date: _____ | Date of Birth: _____ |

| Type of Notarial Act: | ❏ Verbal Ceremony Performed | ❏ Other (Describe): | Fee: $ | |
| ❏ Oath/Affirmation | ❏ Acknowledgment | | Travel: $ | Right Thumbprint of Signer |

| Type of Document | Date of Document | Witness(es) Present | Other Signer(s) Present | |
| | | ❏ Yes ❏ No | ❏ Yes ❏ No | |

| Witness: Printed Name | Address/Phone | Signature of Witness | |

| Comments; Additional Information: | If Notarization Failed or Refused, Give Reason: |
| | ❏ Insufficient ID   ❏ Signer Confused   ❏ Other (Explain in Comments Field) |

146

| Printed Name of Signer: | Signer's Signature: | Time AM/PM: _____ |
| | | Date Notarized: _____ |

| Signer's Complete Address: | City | State | Zip | Phone |

| Identification by: | ❏ Identification Card | Issued By: _____ | I.D. # _____ |
| ❏ Personal Knowledge | ❏ Credible Witness(es) | Type of I.D.: _____ | Expiration Date: _____ | Date of Birth: _____ |

| Type of Notarial Act: | ❏ Verbal Ceremony Performed | ❏ Other (Describe): | Fee: $ | |
| ❏ Oath/Affirmation | ❏ Acknowledgment | | Travel: $ | Right Thumbprint of Signer |

| Type of Document | Date of Document | Witness(es) Present | Other Signer(s) Present | |
| | | ❏ Yes ❏ No | ❏ Yes ❏ No | |

| Witness: Printed Name | Address/Phone | Signature of Witness | |

| Comments; Additional Information: | If Notarization Failed or Refused, Give Reason: |
| | ❏ Insufficient ID   ❏ Signer Confused   ❏ Other (Explain in Comments Field) |

147

| Printed Name of Signer: | Signer's Signature: | Time AM/PM: _____ |
| | | Date Notarized: _____ |

| Signer's Complete Address: | City | State | Zip | Phone |

| Identification by: | ❏ Identification Card | Issued By: _____ | I.D. # _____ |
| ❏ Personal Knowledge | ❏ Credible Witness(es) | Type of I.D.: _____ | Expiration Date: _____ | Date of Birth: _____ |

| Type of Notarial Act: | ❏ Verbal Ceremony Performed | ❏ Other (Describe): | Fee: $ | |
| ❏ Oath/Affirmation | ❏ Acknowledgment | | Travel: $ | Right Thumbprint of Signer |

| Type of Document | Date of Document | Witness(es) Present | Other Signer(s) Present | |
| | | ❏ Yes ❏ No | ❏ Yes ❏ No | |

| Witness: Printed Name | Address/Phone | Signature of Witness | |

| Comments; Additional Information: | If Notarization Failed or Refused, Give Reason: |
| | ❏ Insufficient ID   ❏ Signer Confused   ❏ Other (Explain in Comments Field) |

| Printed Name of Signer: | Signer's Signature: | Time AM/PM: _____ | **148** |
| | | Date Notarized: _____ | |

Signer's Complete Address: City State Zip Phone

Identification by: ❑ Identification Card Issued By: _____ I.D. # _____

❑ Personal Knowledge ❑ Credible Witness(es) Type of I.D.: _____ Expiration Date: _____ Date of Birth: _____

Type of Notarial Act: ❑ Verbal Ceremony Performed ❑ Other (Describe): Fee: $

❑ Oath/Affirmation ❑ Acknowledgment Travel: $

Type of Document Date of Document Witness(es) Present Other Signer(s) Present

❑ Yes ❑ No ❑ Yes ❑ No

Right Thumbprint of Signer

Witness: Printed Name Address/Phone Signature of Witness

Comments; Additional Information: If Notarization Failed or Refused, Give Reason:

❑ Insufficient ID ❑ Signer Confused ❑ Other (Explain in Comments Field)

| Printed Name of Signer: | Signer's Signature: | Time AM/PM: _____ | **149** |
| | | Date Notarized: _____ | |

Signer's Complete Address: City State Zip Phone

Identification by: ❑ Identification Card Issued By: _____ I.D. # _____

❑ Personal Knowledge ❑ Credible Witness(es) Type of I.D.: _____ Expiration Date: _____ Date of Birth: _____

Type of Notarial Act: ❑ Verbal Ceremony Performed ❑ Other (Describe): Fee: $

❑ Oath/Affirmation ❑ Acknowledgment Travel: $

Type of Document Date of Document Witness(es) Present Other Signer(s) Present

❑ Yes ❑ No ❑ Yes ❑ No

Right Thumbprint of Signer

Witness: Printed Name Address/Phone Signature of Witness

Comments; Additional Information: If Notarization Failed or Refused, Give Reason:

❑ Insufficient ID ❑ Signer Confused ❑ Other (Explain in Comments Field)

| Printed Name of Signer: | Signer's Signature: | Time AM/PM: _____ | **150** |
| | | Date Notarized: _____ | |

Signer's Complete Address: City State Zip Phone

Identification by: ❑ Identification Card Issued By: _____ I.D. # _____

❑ Personal Knowledge ❑ Credible Witness(es) Type of I.D.: _____ Expiration Date: _____ Date of Birth: _____

Type of Notarial Act: ❑ Verbal Ceremony Performed ❑ Other (Describe): Fee: $

❑ Oath/Affirmation ❑ Acknowledgment Travel: $

Type of Document Date of Document Witness(es) Present Other Signer(s) Present

❑ Yes ❑ No ❑ Yes ❑ No

Right Thumbprint of Signer

Witness: Printed Name Address/Phone Signature of Witness

Comments; Additional Information: If Notarization Failed or Refused, Give Reason:

❑ Insufficient ID ❑ Signer Confused ❑ Other (Explain in Comments Field)

151

Printed Name of Signer:

Signer's Signature:

Time AM/PM: _____

Date Notarized: _____

Signer's Complete Address:　　　City　　　　　State　　Zip　　　Phone

Identification by: ❏ Identification Card　　Issued By: _____　I.D. # _____

❏ Personal Knowledge　❏ Credible Witness(es)　Type of I.D.: _____　Expiration Date: _____　Date of Birth: _____

Type of Notarial Act: ❏ Verbal Ceremony Performed　❏ Other (Describe):　　Fee: $

❏ Oath/Affirmation　❏ Acknowledgment　　　　　Travel: $

Type of Document　　Date of Document　Witness(es) Present　Other Signer(s) Present

❏ Yes ❏ No　　❏ Yes ❏ No

Witness: Printed Name　　Address/Phone　　Signature of Witness

Right Thumbprint of Signer

Comments; Additional Information:　　If Notarization Failed or Refused, Give Reason:

❏ Insufficient ID　❏ Signer Confused　❏ Other (Explain in Comments Field)

152

Printed Name of Signer:

Signer's Signature:

Time AM/PM: _____

Date Notarized: _____

Signer's Complete Address:　　　City　　　　　State　　Zip　　　Phone

Identification by: ❏ Identification Card　　Issued By: _____　I.D. # _____

❏ Personal Knowledge　❏ Credible Witness(es)　Type of I.D.: _____　Expiration Date: _____　Date of Birth: _____

Type of Notarial Act: ❏ Verbal Ceremony Performed　❏ Other (Describe):　　Fee: $

❏ Oath/Affirmation　❏ Acknowledgment　　　　　Travel: $

Type of Document　　Date of Document　Witness(es) Present　Other Signer(s) Present

❏ Yes ❏ No　　❏ Yes ❏ No

Witness: Printed Name　　Address/Phone　　Signature of Witness

Right Thumbprint of Signer

Comments; Additional Information:　　If Notarization Failed or Refused, Give Reason:

❏ Insufficient ID　❏ Signer Confused　❏ Other (Explain in Comments Field)

153

Printed Name of Signer:

Signer's Signature:

Time AM/PM: _____

Date Notarized: _____

Signer's Complete Address:　　　City　　　　　State　　Zip　　　Phone

Identification by: ❏ Identification Card　　Issued By: _____　I.D. # _____

❏ Personal Knowledge　❏ Credible Witness(es)　Type of I.D.: _____　Expiration Date: _____　Date of Birth: _____

Type of Notarial Act: ❏ Verbal Ceremony Performed　❏ Other (Describe):　　Fee: $

❏ Oath/Affirmation　❏ Acknowledgment　　　　　Travel: $

Type of Document　　Date of Document　Witness(es) Present　Other Signer(s) Present

❏ Yes ❏ No　　❏ Yes ❏ No

Witness: Printed Name　　Address/Phone　　Signature of Witness

Right Thumbprint of Signer

Comments; Additional Information:　　If Notarization Failed or Refused, Give Reason:

❏ Insufficient ID　❏ Signer Confused　❏ Other (Explain in Comments Field)

Printed Name of Signer: | **Signer's Signature:** | **Time AM/PM:** _____ | **154**
Date Notarized: _____

Signer's Complete Address: | **City** | **State** | **Zip** | **Phone**

Identification by: | ❏ Identification Card | **Issued By:** _____ | **I.D. #** _____

❏ **Personal Knowledge** | ❏ Credible Witness(es) | **Type of I.D.:** _____ | **Expiration Date:** _____ | **Date of Birth:** _____

Type of Notarial Act: | ❏ Verbal Ceremony Performed | ❏ Other (Describe): | **Fee: $**
❏ **Oath/Affirmation** | ❏ Acknowledgment | | **Travel: $**

Type of Document | **Date of Document** | **Witness(es) Present** | **Other Signer(s) Present** | Right Thumbprint of Signer
| | ❏ Yes ❏ No | ❏ Yes ❏ No |

Witness: Printed Name | **Address/Phone** | **Signature of Witness**

Comments; Additional Information: | **If Notarization Failed or Refused, Give Reason:**
❏ Insufficient ID ❏ Signer Confused ❏ Other (Explain in Comments Field)

Printed Name of Signer: | **Signer's Signature:** | **Time AM/PM:** _____ | **155**
Date Notarized: _____

Signer's Complete Address: | **City** | **State** | **Zip** | **Phone**

Identification by: | ❏ Identification Card | **Issued By:** _____ | **I.D. #** _____

❏ **Personal Knowledge** | ❏ Credible Witness(es) | **Type of I.D.:** _____ | **Expiration Date:** _____ | **Date of Birth:** _____

Type of Notarial Act: | ❏ Verbal Ceremony Performed | ❏ Other (Describe): | **Fee: $**
❏ **Oath/Affirmation** | ❏ Acknowledgment | | **Travel: $**

Type of Document | **Date of Document** | **Witness(es) Present** | **Other Signer(s) Present** | Right Thumbprint of Signer
| | ❏ Yes ❏ No | ❏ Yes ❏ No |

Witness: Printed Name | **Address/Phone** | **Signature of Witness**

Comments; Additional Information: | **If Notarization Failed or Refused, Give Reason:**
❏ Insufficient ID ❏ Signer Confused ❏ Other (Explain in Comments Field)

Printed Name of Signer: | **Signer's Signature:** | **Time AM/PM:** _____ | **156**
Date Notarized: _____

Signer's Complete Address: | **City** | **State** | **Zip** | **Phone**

Identification by: | ❏ Identification Card | **Issued By:** _____ | **I.D. #** _____

❏ **Personal Knowledge** | ❏ Credible Witness(es) | **Type of I.D.:** _____ | **Expiration Date:** _____ | **Date of Birth:** _____

Type of Notarial Act: | ❏ Verbal Ceremony Performed | ❏ Other (Describe): | **Fee: $**
❏ **Oath/Affirmation** | ❏ Acknowledgment | | **Travel: $**

Type of Document | **Date of Document** | **Witness(es) Present** | **Other Signer(s) Present** | Right Thumbprint of Signer
| | ❏ Yes ❏ No | ❏ Yes ❏ No |

Witness: Printed Name | **Address/Phone** | **Signature of Witness**

Comments; Additional Information: | **If Notarization Failed or Refused, Give Reason:**
❏ Insufficient ID ❏ Signer Confused ❏ Other (Explain in Comments Field)

157

| Printed Name of Signer: | Signer's Signature: | Time AM/PM: _____ |
| | | Date Notarized: _____ |

| Signer's Complete Address: | City | State | Zip | Phone |

| Identification by: | ❏ Identification Card | Issued By: _____ | I.D. # _____ |
| ❏ Personal Knowledge | ❏ Credible Witness(es) | Type of I.D.: _____ | Expiration Date: _____ | Date of Birth: _____ |

| Type of Notarial Act: | ❏ Verbal Ceremony Performed | ❏ Other (Describe): | Fee: $ | Right Thumbprint of Signer |
| ❏ Oath/Affirmation | ❏ Acknowledgment | | Travel: $ | |

| Type of Document | Date of Document | Witness(es) Present ❏ Yes ❏ No | Other Signer(s) Present ❏ Yes ❏ No | |

| Witness: Printed Name | Address/Phone | Signature of Witness | |

| Comments; Additional Information: | If Notarization Failed or Refused, Give Reason: |
| | ❏ Insufficient ID ❏ Signer Confused ❏ Other (Explain in Comments Field) |

158

| Printed Name of Signer: | Signer's Signature: | Time AM/PM: _____ |
| | | Date Notarized: _____ |

| Signer's Complete Address: | City | State | Zip | Phone |

| Identification by: | ❏ Identification Card | Issued By: _____ | I.D. # _____ |
| ❏ Personal Knowledge | ❏ Credible Witness(es) | Type of I.D.: _____ | Expiration Date: _____ | Date of Birth: _____ |

| Type of Notarial Act: | ❏ Verbal Ceremony Performed | ❏ Other (Describe): | Fee: $ | Right Thumbprint of Signer |
| ❏ Oath/Affirmation | ❏ Acknowledgment | | Travel: $ | |

| Type of Document | Date of Document | Witness(es) Present ❏ Yes ❏ No | Other Signer(s) Present ❏ Yes ❏ No | |

| Witness: Printed Name | Address/Phone | Signature of Witness | |

| Comments; Additional Information: | If Notarization Failed or Refused, Give Reason: |
| | ❏ Insufficient ID ❏ Signer Confused ❏ Other (Explain in Comments Field) |

159

| Printed Name of Signer: | Signer's Signature: | Time AM/PM: _____ |
| | | Date Notarized: _____ |

| Signer's Complete Address: | City | State | Zip | Phone |

| Identification by: | ❏ Identification Card | Issued By: _____ | I.D. # _____ |
| ❏ Personal Knowledge | ❏ Credible Witness(es) | Type of I.D.: _____ | Expiration Date: _____ | Date of Birth: _____ |

| Type of Notarial Act: | ❏ Verbal Ceremony Performed | ❏ Other (Describe): | Fee: $ | Right Thumbprint of Signer |
| ❏ Oath/Affirmation | ❏ Acknowledgment | | Travel: $ | |

| Type of Document | Date of Document | Witness(es) Present ❏ Yes ❏ No | Other Signer(s) Present ❏ Yes ❏ No | |

| Witness: Printed Name | Address/Phone | Signature of Witness | |

| Comments; Additional Information: | If Notarization Failed or Refused, Give Reason: |
| | ❏ Insufficient ID ❏ Signer Confused ❏ Other (Explain in Comments Field) |

160

Printed Name of Signer:

Signer's Signature:

Time AM/PM: _____

Date Notarized: _____

Signer's Complete Address: City   State   Zip   Phone

Identification by: ❑ Identification Card   Issued By: _____   I.D. # _____

❑ Personal Knowledge   ❑ Credible Witness(es)   Type of I.D.: _____   Expiration Date: _____   Date of Birth: _____

Type of Notarial Act: ❑ Verbal Ceremony Performed   ❑ Other (Describe):   **Fee:** $ _____

❑ Oath/Affirmation   ❑ Acknowledgment   **Travel:** $ _____

Type of Document   Date of Document   Witness(es) Present ❑ Yes ❑ No   Other Signer(s) Present ❑ Yes ❑ No   *Right Thumbprint of Signer*

Witness: Printed Name   Address/Phone   Signature of Witness

Comments; Additional Information: If Notarization Failed or Refused, Give Reason:

❑ Insufficient ID   ❑ Signer Confused   ❑ Other (Explain in Comments Field)

161

Printed Name of Signer:

Signer's Signature:

Time AM/PM: _____

Date Notarized: _____

Signer's Complete Address: City   State   Zip   Phone

Identification by: ❑ Identification Card   Issued By: _____   I.D. # _____

❑ Personal Knowledge   ❑ Credible Witness(es)   Type of I.D.: _____   Expiration Date: _____   Date of Birth: _____

Type of Notarial Act: ❑ Verbal Ceremony Performed   ❑ Other (Describe):   **Fee:** $ _____

❑ Oath/Affirmation   ❑ Acknowledgment   **Travel:** $ _____

Type of Document   Date of Document   Witness(es) Present ❑ Yes ❑ No   Other Signer(s) Present ❑ Yes ❑ No   *Right Thumbprint of Signer*

Witness: Printed Name   Address/Phone   Signature of Witness

Comments; Additional Information: If Notarization Failed or Refused, Give Reason:

❑ Insufficient ID   ❑ Signer Confused   ❑ Other (Explain in Comments Field)

162

Printed Name of Signer:

Signer's Signature:

Time AM/PM: _____

Date Notarized: _____

Signer's Complete Address: City   State   Zip   Phone

Identification by: ❑ Identification Card   Issued By: _____   I.D. # _____

❑ Personal Knowledge   ❑ Credible Witness(es)   Type of I.D.: _____   Expiration Date: _____   Date of Birth: _____

Type of Notarial Act: ❑ Verbal Ceremony Performed   ❑ Other (Describe):   **Fee:** $ _____

❑ Oath/Affirmation   ❑ Acknowledgment   **Travel:** $ _____

Type of Document   Date of Document   Witness(es) Present ❑ Yes ❑ No   Other Signer(s) Present ❑ Yes ❑ No   *Right Thumbprint of Signer*

Witness: Printed Name   Address/Phone   Signature of Witness

Comments; Additional Information: If Notarization Failed or Refused, Give Reason:

❑ Insufficient ID   ❑ Signer Confused   ❑ Other (Explain in Comments Field)

163

Printed Name of Signer:	Signer's Signature:	Time AM/PM: _____
		Date Notarized: _____

Signer's Complete Address: City State Zip Phone

Identification by: ☐ Identification Card Issued By: _____ I.D. # _____

☐ Personal Knowledge ☐ Credible Witness(es) Type of I.D.:_____ Expiration Date: _____ Date of Birth: _____

Type of Notarial Act: ☐ Verbal Ceremony Performed ☐ Other (Describe): Fee: $

☐ Oath/Affirmation ☐ Acknowledgment Travel: $

Type of Document Date of Document Witness(es) Present Other Signer(s) Present

Right Thumbprint of Signer

☐ Yes ☐ No ☐ Yes ☐ No

Witness: Printed Name Address/Phone Signature of Witness

Comments; Additional Information: If Notarization Failed or Refused, Give Reason:

☐ Insufficient ID ☐ Signer Confused ☐ Other (Explain in Comments Field)

164

Printed Name of Signer:	Signer's Signature:	Time AM/PM: _____
		Date Notarized: _____

Signer's Complete Address: City State Zip Phone

Identification by: ☐ Identification Card Issued By: _____ I.D. # _____

☐ Personal Knowledge ☐ Credible Witness(es) Type of I.D.:_____ Expiration Date: _____ Date of Birth: _____

Type of Notarial Act: ☐ Verbal Ceremony Performed ☐ Other (Describe): Fee: $

☐ Oath/Affirmation ☐ Acknowledgment Travel: $

Type of Document Date of Document Witness(es) Present Other Signer(s) Present

Right Thumbprint of Signer

☐ Yes ☐ No ☐ Yes ☐ No

Witness: Printed Name Address/Phone Signature of Witness

Comments; Additional Information: If Notarization Failed or Refused, Give Reason:

☐ Insufficient ID ☐ Signer Confused ☐ Other (Explain in Comments Field)

165

Printed Name of Signer:	Signer's Signature:	Time AM/PM: _____
		Date Notarized: _____

Signer's Complete Address: City State Zip Phone

Identification by: ☐ Identification Card Issued By: _____ I.D. # _____

☐ Personal Knowledge ☐ Credible Witness(es) Type of I.D.:_____ Expiration Date: _____ Date of Birth: _____

Type of Notarial Act: ☐ Verbal Ceremony Performed ☐ Other (Describe): Fee: $

☐ Oath/Affirmation ☐ Acknowledgment Travel: $

Type of Document Date of Document Witness(es) Present Other Signer(s) Present

Right Thumbprint of Signer

☐ Yes ☐ No ☐ Yes ☐ No

Witness: Printed Name Address/Phone Signature of Witness

Comments; Additional Information: If Notarization Failed or Refused, Give Reason:

☐ Insufficient ID ☐ Signer Confused ☐ Other (Explain in Comments Field)

166

| Printed Name of Signer: | Signer's Signature: | Time AM/PM: _____ |
| | | Date Notarized: _____ |

| Signer's Complete Address: | City | State | Zip | Phone |

| Identification by: | ☐ Identification Card | Issued By: _____ | I.D. # _____ |
| ☐ Personal Knowledge | ☐ Credible Witness(es) | Type of I.D.: _____ | Expiration Date: _____ | Date of Birth: _____ |

| Type of Notarial Act: | ☐ Verbal Ceremony Performed | ☐ Other (Describe): | Fee: $ | |
| ☐ Oath/Affirmation | ☐ Acknowledgment | | Travel: $ | |

| Type of Document | Date of Document | Witness(es) Present | Other Signer(s) Present | Right Thumbprint of Signer |
| | | ☐ Yes ☐ No | ☐ Yes ☐ No | |

| Witness: Printed Name | Address/Phone | Signature of Witness | |

| Comments; Additional Information: | If Notarization Failed or Refused, Give Reason: |
| | ☐ Insufficient ID   ☐ Signer Confused   ☐ Other (Explain in Comments Field) |

167

| Printed Name of Signer: | Signer's Signature: | Time AM/PM: _____ |
| | | Date Notarized: _____ |

| Signer's Complete Address: | City | State | Zip | Phone |

| Identification by: | ☐ Identification Card | Issued By: _____ | I.D. # _____ |
| ☐ Personal Knowledge | ☐ Credible Witness(es) | Type of I.D.: _____ | Expiration Date: _____ | Date of Birth: _____ |

| Type of Notarial Act: | ☐ Verbal Ceremony Performed | ☐ Other (Describe): | Fee: $ | |
| ☐ Oath/Affirmation | ☐ Acknowledgment | | Travel: $ | |

| Type of Document | Date of Document | Witness(es) Present | Other Signer(s) Present | Right Thumbprint of Signer |
| | | ☐ Yes ☐ No | ☐ Yes ☐ No | |

| Witness: Printed Name | Address/Phone | Signature of Witness | |

| Comments; Additional Information: | If Notarization Failed or Refused, Give Reason: |
| | ☐ Insufficient ID   ☐ Signer Confused   ☐ Other (Explain in Comments Field) |

168

| Printed Name of Signer: | Signer's Signature: | Time AM/PM: _____ |
| | | Date Notarized: _____ |

| Signer's Complete Address: | City | State | Zip | Phone |

| Identification by: | ☐ Identification Card | Issued By: _____ | I.D. # _____ |
| ☐ Personal Knowledge | ☐ Credible Witness(es) | Type of I.D.: _____ | Expiration Date: _____ | Date of Birth: _____ |

| Type of Notarial Act: | ☐ Verbal Ceremony Performed | ☐ Other (Describe): | Fee: $ | |
| ☐ Oath/Affirmation | ☐ Acknowledgment | | Travel: $ | |

| Type of Document | Date of Document | Witness(es) Present | Other Signer(s) Present | Right Thumbprint of Signer |
| | | ☐ Yes ☐ No | ☐ Yes ☐ No | |

| Witness: Printed Name | Address/Phone | Signature of Witness | |

| Comments; Additional Information: | If Notarization Failed or Refused, Give Reason: |
| | ☐ Insufficient ID   ☐ Signer Confused   ☐ Other (Explain in Comments Field) |

169

| Printed Name of Signer: | Signer's Signature: | Time AM/PM: _____ |
| | | Date Notarized: _____ |

| Signer's Complete Address: | City | State | Zip | Phone |

Identification by: ❑ Identification Card   Issued By: _____   I.D. # _____

❑ Personal Knowledge   ❑ Credible Witness(es)   Type of I.D.: _____   Expiration Date: _____   Date of Birth: _____

Type of Notarial Act: ❑ Verbal Ceremony Performed   ❑ Other (Describe):   Fee: $

❑ Oath/Affirmation   ❑ Acknowledgment   Travel: $

Type of Document   Date of Document   Witness(es) Present ❑ Yes ❑ No   Other Signer(s) Present ❑ Yes ❑ No

Right Thumbprint of Signer

Witness: Printed Name   Address/Phone   Signature of Witness

Comments; Additional Information: If Notarization Failed or Refused, Give Reason:

❑ Insufficient ID   ❑ Signer Confused   ❑ Other (Explain in Comments Field)

170

| Printed Name of Signer: | Signer's Signature: | Time AM/PM: _____ |
| | | Date Notarized: _____ |

| Signer's Complete Address: | City | State | Zip | Phone |

Identification by: ❑ Identification Card   Issued By: _____   I.D. # _____

❑ Personal Knowledge   ❑ Credible Witness(es)   Type of I.D.: _____   Expiration Date: _____   Date of Birth: _____

Type of Notarial Act: ❑ Verbal Ceremony Performed   ❑ Other (Describe):   Fee: $

❑ Oath/Affirmation   ❑ Acknowledgment   Travel: $

Type of Document   Date of Document   Witness(es) Present ❑ Yes ❑ No   Other Signer(s) Present ❑ Yes ❑ No

Right Thumbprint of Signer

Witness: Printed Name   Address/Phone   Signature of Witness

Comments; Additional Information: If Notarization Failed or Refused, Give Reason:

❑ Insufficient ID   ❑ Signer Confused   ❑ Other (Explain in Comments Field)

171

| Printed Name of Signer: | Signer's Signature: | Time AM/PM: _____ |
| | | Date Notarized: _____ |

| Signer's Complete Address: | City | State | Zip | Phone |

Identification by: ❑ Identification Card   Issued By: _____   I.D. # _____

❑ Personal Knowledge   ❑ Credible Witness(es)   Type of I.D.: _____   Expiration Date: _____   Date of Birth: _____

Type of Notarial Act: ❑ Verbal Ceremony Performed   ❑ Other (Describe):   Fee: $

❑ Oath/Affirmation   ❑ Acknowledgment   Travel: $

Type of Document   Date of Document   Witness(es) Present ❑ Yes ❑ No   Other Signer(s) Present ❑ Yes ❑ No

Right Thumbprint of Signer

Witness: Printed Name   Address/Phone   Signature of Witness

Comments; Additional Information: If Notarization Failed or Refused, Give Reason:

❑ Insufficient ID   ❑ Signer Confused   ❑ Other (Explain in Comments Field)

172

| Printed Name of Signer: | Signer's Signature: | Time AM/PM: _____ |
| | | Date Notarized: _____ |

| Signer's Complete Address: | City | State | Zip | Phone |

| Identification by: | ❑ Identification Card | Issued By: _____ | I.D. # _____ |
| ❑ Personal Knowledge | ❑ Credible Witness(es) | Type of I.D.: _____ | Expiration Date: _____ | Date of Birth: _____ |

| Type of Notarial Act: | ❑ Verbal Ceremony Performed | ❑ Other (Describe): | Fee: $ | |
| ❑ Oath/Affirmation | ❑ Acknowledgment | | Travel: $ | Right Thumbprint of Signer |

| Type of Document | Date of Document | Witness(es) Present | Other Signer(s) Present | |
| | | ❑ Yes ❑ No | ❑ Yes ❑ No | |

| Witness: Printed Name | Address/Phone | Signature of Witness | |

| Comments; Additional Information: | If Notarization Failed or Refused, Give Reason: |
| | ❑ Insufficient ID ❑ Signer Confused ❑ Other (Explain in Comments Field) |

173

| Printed Name of Signer: | Signer's Signature: | Time AM/PM: _____ |
| | | Date Notarized: _____ |

| Signer's Complete Address: | City | State | Zip | Phone |

| Identification by: | ❑ Identification Card | Issued By: _____ | I.D. # _____ |
| ❑ Personal Knowledge | ❑ Credible Witness(es) | Type of I.D.: _____ | Expiration Date: _____ | Date of Birth: _____ |

| Type of Notarial Act: | ❑ Verbal Ceremony Performed | ❑ Other (Describe): | Fee: $ | |
| ❑ Oath/Affirmation | ❑ Acknowledgment | | Travel: $ | Right Thumbprint of Signer |

| Type of Document | Date of Document | Witness(es) Present | Other Signer(s) Present | |
| | | ❑ Yes ❑ No | ❑ Yes ❑ No | |

| Witness: Printed Name | Address/Phone | Signature of Witness | |

| Comments; Additional Information: | If Notarization Failed or Refused, Give Reason: |
| | ❑ Insufficient ID ❑ Signer Confused ❑ Other (Explain in Comments Field) |

174

| Printed Name of Signer: | Signer's Signature: | Time AM/PM: _____ |
| | | Date Notarized: _____ |

| Signer's Complete Address: | City | State | Zip | Phone |

| Identification by: | ❑ Identification Card | Issued By: _____ | I.D. # _____ |
| ❑ Personal Knowledge | ❑ Credible Witness(es) | Type of I.D.: _____ | Expiration Date: _____ | Date of Birth: _____ |

| Type of Notarial Act: | ❑ Verbal Ceremony Performed | ❑ Other (Describe): | Fee: $ | |
| ❑ Oath/Affirmation | ❑ Acknowledgment | | Travel: $ | Right Thumbprint of Signer |

| Type of Document | Date of Document | Witness(es) Present | Other Signer(s) Present | |
| | | ❑ Yes ❑ No | ❑ Yes ❑ No | |

| Witness: Printed Name | Address/Phone | Signature of Witness | |

| Comments; Additional Information: | If Notarization Failed or Refused, Give Reason: |
| | ❑ Insufficient ID ❑ Signer Confused ❑ Other (Explain in Comments Field) |

175

Printed Name of Signer: _____

Signer's Signature: _____

Time AM/PM: _____
Date Notarized: _____

Signer's Complete Address: _____   City _____   State ___   Zip ___   Phone _____

Identification by: ❏ Identification Card   Issued By: _____   I.D. # _____

❏ Personal Knowledge   ❏ Credible Witness(es)   Type of I.D.: _____   Expiration Date: _____   Date of Birth: _____

Type of Notarial Act: ❏ Verbal Ceremony Performed   ❏ Other (Describe): _____   Fee: $ _____   Travel: $ _____

❏ Oath/Affirmation   ❏ Acknowledgment

Type of Document _____   Date of Document _____   Witness(es) Present ❏ Yes ❏ No   Other Signer(s) Present ❏ Yes ❏ No

Right Thumbprint of Signer

Witness: Printed Name _____   Address/Phone _____   Signature of Witness _____

Comments; Additional Information: _____

If Notarization Failed or Refused, Give Reason:

❏ Insufficient ID   ❏ Signer Confused   ❏ Other (Explain in Comments Field)

176

Printed Name of Signer: _____

Signer's Signature: _____

Time AM/PM: _____
Date Notarized: _____

Signer's Complete Address: _____   City _____   State ___   Zip ___   Phone _____

Identification by: ❏ Identification Card   Issued By: _____   I.D. # _____

❏ Personal Knowledge   ❏ Credible Witness(es)   Type of I.D.: _____   Expiration Date: _____   Date of Birth: _____

Type of Notarial Act: ❏ Verbal Ceremony Performed   ❏ Other (Describe): _____   Fee: $ _____   Travel: $ _____

❏ Oath/Affirmation   ❏ Acknowledgment

Type of Document _____   Date of Document _____   Witness(es) Present ❏ Yes ❏ No   Other Signer(s) Present ❏ Yes ❏ No

Right Thumbprint of Signer

Witness: Printed Name _____   Address/Phone _____   Signature of Witness _____

Comments; Additional Information: _____

If Notarization Failed or Refused, Give Reason:

❏ Insufficient ID   ❏ Signer Confused   ❏ Other (Explain in Comments Field)

177

Printed Name of Signer: _____

Signer's Signature: _____

Time AM/PM: _____
Date Notarized: _____

Signer's Complete Address: _____   City _____   State ___   Zip ___   Phone _____

Identification by: ❏ Identification Card   Issued By: _____   I.D. # _____

❏ Personal Knowledge   ❏ Credible Witness(es)   Type of I.D.: _____   Expiration Date: _____   Date of Birth: _____

Type of Notarial Act: ❏ Verbal Ceremony Performed   ❏ Other (Describe): _____   Fee: $ _____   Travel: $ _____

❏ Oath/Affirmation   ❏ Acknowledgment

Type of Document _____   Date of Document _____   Witness(es) Present ❏ Yes ❏ No   Other Signer(s) Present ❏ Yes ❏ No

Right Thumbprint of Signer

Witness: Printed Name _____   Address/Phone _____   Signature of Witness _____

Comments; Additional Information: _____

If Notarization Failed or Refused, Give Reason:

❏ Insufficient ID   ❏ Signer Confused   ❏ Other (Explain in Comments Field)

| Printed Name of Signer: | Signer's Signature: | Time AM/PM: _____ **178** |
| | | Date Notarized: _____ |

Signer's Complete Address: City   State   Zip   Phone

Identification by: ❏ Identification Card   Issued By: _____   I.D. # _____

❏ Personal Knowledge   ❏ Credible Witness(es)   Type of I.D.: _____   Expiration Date: _____   Date of Birth: _____

Type of Notarial Act: ❏ Verbal Ceremony Performed   ❏ Other (Describe):   Fee: $

❏ Oath/Affirmation   ❏ Acknowledgment   Travel: $

Type of Document   Date of Document   Witness(es) Present   Other Signer(s) Present

❏ Yes ❏ No   ❏ Yes ❏ No

Right Thumbprint of Signer

Witness: Printed Name   Address/Phone   Signature of Witness

Comments; Additional Information:

If Notarization Failed or Refused, Give Reason:

❏ Insufficient ID   ❏ Signer Confused   ❏ Other (Explain in Comments Field)

| Printed Name of Signer: | Signer's Signature: | Time AM/PM: _____ **179** |
| | | Date Notarized: _____ |

Signer's Complete Address: City   State   Zip   Phone

Identification by: ❏ Identification Card   Issued By: _____   I.D. # _____

❏ Personal Knowledge   ❏ Credible Witness(es)   Type of I.D.: _____   Expiration Date: _____   Date of Birth: _____

Type of Notarial Act: ❏ Verbal Ceremony Performed   ❏ Other (Describe):   Fee: $

❏ Oath/Affirmation   ❏ Acknowledgment   Travel: $

Type of Document   Date of Document   Witness(es) Present   Other Signer(s) Present

❏ Yes ❏ No   ❏ Yes ❏ No

Right Thumbprint of Signer

Witness: Printed Name   Address/Phone   Signature of Witness

Comments; Additional Information:

If Notarization Failed or Refused, Give Reason:

❏ Insufficient ID   ❏ Signer Confused   ❏ Other (Explain in Comments Field)

| Printed Name of Signer: | Signer's Signature: | Time AM/PM: _____ **180** |
| | | Date Notarized: _____ |

Signer's Complete Address: City   State   Zip   Phone

Identification by: ❏ Identification Card   Issued By: _____   I.D. # _____

❏ Personal Knowledge   ❏ Credible Witness(es)   Type of I.D.: _____   Expiration Date: _____   Date of Birth: _____

Type of Notarial Act: ❏ Verbal Ceremony Performed   ❏ Other (Describe):   Fee: $

❏ Oath/Affirmation   ❏ Acknowledgment   Travel: $

Type of Document   Date of Document   Witness(es) Present   Other Signer(s) Present

❏ Yes ❏ No   ❏ Yes ❏ No

Right Thumbprint of Signer

Witness: Printed Name   Address/Phone   Signature of Witness

Comments; Additional Information:

If Notarization Failed or Refused, Give Reason:

❏ Insufficient ID   ❏ Signer Confused   ❏ Other (Explain in Comments Field)

181

| Printed Name of Signer: | Signer's Signature: | Time AM/PM: _____ |
| | | Date Notarized: _____ |

Signer's Complete Address: City State Zip Phone

Identification by: ❑ Identification Card Issued By: _____ I.D. # _____

❑ Personal Knowledge ❑ Credible Witness(es) Type of I.D.: _____ Expiration Date: _____ Date of Birth: _____

Type of Notarial Act: ❑ Verbal Ceremony Performed ❑ Other (Describe): Fee: $

❑ Oath/Affirmation ❑ Acknowledgment Travel: $

Type of Document Date of Document Witness(es) Present Other Signer(s) Present

❑ Yes ❑ No ❑ Yes ❑ No

Right Thumbprint of Signer

Witness: Printed Name Address/Phone Signature of Witness

Comments; Additional Information: If Notarization Failed or Refused, Give Reason:

❑ Insufficient ID ❑ Signer Confused ❑ Other (Explain in Comments Field)

182

| Printed Name of Signer: | Signer's Signature: | Time AM/PM: _____ |
| | | Date Notarized: _____ |

Signer's Complete Address: City State Zip Phone

Identification by: ❑ Identification Card Issued By: _____ I.D. # _____

❑ Personal Knowledge ❑ Credible Witness(es) Type of I.D.: _____ Expiration Date: _____ Date of Birth: _____

Type of Notarial Act: ❑ Verbal Ceremony Performed ❑ Other (Describe): Fee: $

❑ Oath/Affirmation ❑ Acknowledgment Travel: $

Type of Document Date of Document Witness(es) Present Other Signer(s) Present

❑ Yes ❑ No ❑ Yes ❑ No

Right Thumbprint of Signer

Witness: Printed Name Address/Phone Signature of Witness

Comments; Additional Information: If Notarization Failed or Refused, Give Reason:

❑ Insufficient ID ❑ Signer Confused ❑ Other (Explain in Comments Field)

183

| Printed Name of Signer: | Signer's Signature: | Time AM/PM: _____ |
| | | Date Notarized: _____ |

Signer's Complete Address: City State Zip Phone

Identification by: ❑ Identification Card Issued By: _____ I.D. # _____

❑ Personal Knowledge ❑ Credible Witness(es) Type of I.D.: _____ Expiration Date: _____ Date of Birth: _____

Type of Notarial Act: ❑ Verbal Ceremony Performed ❑ Other (Describe): Fee: $

❑ Oath/Affirmation ❑ Acknowledgment Travel: $

Type of Document Date of Document Witness(es) Present Other Signer(s) Present

❑ Yes ❑ No ❑ Yes ❑ No

Right Thumbprint of Signer

Witness: Printed Name Address/Phone Signature of Witness

Comments; Additional Information: If Notarization Failed or Refused, Give Reason:

❑ Insufficient ID ❑ Signer Confused ❑ Other (Explain in Comments Field)

184

| Printed Name of Signer: | Signer's Signature: | Time AM/PM: _____ |
| | | Date Notarized: _____ |

| Signer's Complete Address: | City | State | Zip | Phone |

| Identification by: | ❏ Identification Card | Issued By: _____ | I.D. #_____ |
| ❏ Personal Knowledge | ❏ Credible Witness(es) | Type of I.D.:_____ | Expiration Date: _____ | Date of Birth: _____ |

| Type of Notarial Act: | ❏ Verbal Ceremony Performed | ❏ Other (Describe): | Fee: $ | |
| ❏ Oath/Affirmation | ❏ Acknowledgment | | Travel: $ | |

| Type of Document | Date of Document | Witness(es) Present | Other Signer(s) Present |
| | | ❏ Yes ❏ No | ❏ Yes ❏ No |

| Witness: Printed Name | Address/Phone | Signature of Witness |

Right Thumbprint of Signer

| Comments; Additional Information: | If Notarization Failed or Refused, Give Reason: |
| | ❏ Insufficient ID ❏ Signer Confused ❏ Other (Explain in Comments Field) |

185

| Printed Name of Signer: | Signer's Signature: | Time AM/PM: _____ |
| | | Date Notarized: _____ |

| Signer's Complete Address: | City | State | Zip | Phone |

| Identification by: | ❏ Identification Card | Issued By: _____ | I.D. #_____ |
| ❏ Personal Knowledge | ❏ Credible Witness(es) | Type of I.D.:_____ | Expiration Date: _____ | Date of Birth: _____ |

| Type of Notarial Act: | ❏ Verbal Ceremony Performed | ❏ Other (Describe): | Fee: $ | |
| ❏ Oath/Affirmation | ❏ Acknowledgment | | Travel: $ | |

| Type of Document | Date of Document | Witness(es) Present | Other Signer(s) Present |
| | | ❏ Yes ❏ No | ❏ Yes ❏ No |

| Witness: Printed Name | Address/Phone | Signature of Witness |

Right Thumbprint of Signer

| Comments; Additional Information: | If Notarization Failed or Refused, Give Reason: |
| | ❏ Insufficient ID ❏ Signer Confused ❏ Other (Explain in Comments Field) |

186

| Printed Name of Signer: | Signer's Signature: | Time AM/PM: _____ |
| | | Date Notarized: _____ |

| Signer's Complete Address: | City | State | Zip | Phone |

| Identification by: | ❏ Identification Card | Issued By: _____ | I.D. #_____ |
| ❏ Personal Knowledge | ❏ Credible Witness(es) | Type of I.D.:_____ | Expiration Date: _____ | Date of Birth: _____ |

| Type of Notarial Act: | ❏ Verbal Ceremony Performed | ❏ Other (Describe): | Fee: $ | |
| ❏ Oath/Affirmation | ❏ Acknowledgment | | Travel: $ | |

| Type of Document | Date of Document | Witness(es) Present | Other Signer(s) Present |
| | | ❏ Yes ❏ No | ❏ Yes ❏ No |

| Witness: Printed Name | Address/Phone | Signature of Witness |

Right Thumbprint of Signer

| Comments; Additional Information: | If Notarization Failed or Refused, Give Reason: |
| | ❏ Insufficient ID ❏ Signer Confused ❏ Other (Explain in Comments Field) |

187

| Printed Name of Signer: | Signer's Signature: | Time AM/PM: _____ |
| | | Date Notarized: _____ |

| Signer's Complete Address: | City | State | Zip | Phone |

Identification by: ❏ Identification Card   Issued By: _____   I.D. # _____

❏ Personal Knowledge   ❏ Credible Witness(es)   Type of I.D.: _____   Expiration Date: _____   Date of Birth: _____

| Type of Notarial Act: | ❏ Verbal Ceremony Performed | ❏ Other (Describe): | Fee: $ | |
| ❏ Oath/Affirmation | ❏ Acknowledgment | | Travel: $ | Right Thumbprint of Signer |

| Type of Document | Date of Document | Witness(es) Present ❏ Yes ❏ No | Other Signer(s) Present ❏ Yes ❏ No | |

| Witness: Printed Name | Address/Phone | Signature of Witness | |

Comments; Additional Information:

If Notarization Failed or Refused, Give Reason:

❏ Insufficient ID   ❏ Signer Confused   ❏ Other (Explain in Comments Field)

188

| Printed Name of Signer: | Signer's Signature: | Time AM/PM: _____ |
| | | Date Notarized: _____ |

| Signer's Complete Address: | City | State | Zip | Phone |

Identification by: ❏ Identification Card   Issued By: _____   I.D. # _____

❏ Personal Knowledge   ❏ Credible Witness(es)   Type of I.D.: _____   Expiration Date: _____   Date of Birth: _____

| Type of Notarial Act: | ❏ Verbal Ceremony Performed | ❏ Other (Describe): | Fee: $ | |
| ❏ Oath/Affirmation | ❏ Acknowledgment | | Travel: $ | Right Thumbprint of Signer |

| Type of Document | Date of Document | Witness(es) Present ❏ Yes ❏ No | Other Signer(s) Present ❏ Yes ❏ No | |

| Witness: Printed Name | Address/Phone | Signature of Witness | |

Comments; Additional Information:

If Notarization Failed or Refused, Give Reason:

❏ Insufficient ID   ❏ Signer Confused   ❏ Other (Explain in Comments Field)

189

| Printed Name of Signer: | Signer's Signature: | Time AM/PM: _____ |
| | | Date Notarized: _____ |

| Signer's Complete Address: | City | State | Zip | Phone |

Identification by: ❏ Identification Card   Issued By: _____   I.D. # _____

❏ Personal Knowledge   ❏ Credible Witness(es)   Type of I.D.: _____   Expiration Date: _____   Date of Birth: _____

| Type of Notarial Act: | ❏ Verbal Ceremony Performed | ❏ Other (Describe): | Fee: $ | |
| ❏ Oath/Affirmation | ❏ Acknowledgment | | Travel: $ | Right Thumbprint of Signer |

| Type of Document | Date of Document | Witness(es) Present ❏ Yes ❏ No | Other Signer(s) Present ❏ Yes ❏ No | |

| Witness: Printed Name | Address/Phone | Signature of Witness | |

Comments; Additional Information:

If Notarization Failed or Refused, Give Reason:

❏ Insufficient ID   ❏ Signer Confused   ❏ Other (Explain in Comments Field)

190

Printed Name of Signer: Signer's Signature: Time AM/PM: _____
                                                                                 Date Notarized: _____

Signer's Complete Address: City   State   Zip   Phone

Identification by: ❏ Identification Card   Issued By: _____   I.D. # _____

❏ Personal Knowledge   ❏ Credible Witness(es)   Type of I.D.: _____   Expiration Date: _____   Date of Birth: _____

Type of Notarial Act: ❏ Verbal Ceremony Performed   ❏ Other (Describe):   Fee: $
❏ Oath/Affirmation   ❏ Acknowledgment   Travel: $

Type of Document   Date of Document   Witness(es) Present   Other Signer(s) Present
                                                        ❏ Yes ❏ No   ❏ Yes ❏ No

Witness: Printed Name   Address/Phone   Signature of Witness

Right Thumbprint of Signer

Comments; Additional Information: If Notarization Failed or Refused, Give Reason:

                                                        ❏ Insufficient ID   ❏ Signer Confused   ❏ Other (Explain in Comments Field)

191

Printed Name of Signer: Signer's Signature: Time AM/PM: _____
                                                                                 Date Notarized: _____

Signer's Complete Address: City   State   Zip   Phone

Identification by: ❏ Identification Card   Issued By: _____   I.D. # _____

❏ Personal Knowledge   ❏ Credible Witness(es)   Type of I.D.: _____   Expiration Date: _____   Date of Birth: _____

Type of Notarial Act: ❏ Verbal Ceremony Performed   ❏ Other (Describe):   Fee: $
❏ Oath/Affirmation   ❏ Acknowledgment   Travel: $

Type of Document   Date of Document   Witness(es) Present   Other Signer(s) Present
                                                        ❏ Yes ❏ No   ❏ Yes ❏ No

Witness: Printed Name   Address/Phone   Signature of Witness

Right Thumbprint of Signer

Comments; Additional Information: If Notarization Failed or Refused, Give Reason:

                                                        ❏ Insufficient ID   ❏ Signer Confused   ❏ Other (Explain in Comments Field)

192

Printed Name of Signer: Signer's Signature: Time AM/PM: _____
                                                                                 Date Notarized: _____

Signer's Complete Address: City   State   Zip   Phone

Identification by: ❏ Identification Card   Issued By: _____   I.D. # _____

❏ Personal Knowledge   ❏ Credible Witness(es)   Type of I.D.: _____   Expiration Date: _____   Date of Birth: _____

Type of Notarial Act: ❏ Verbal Ceremony Performed   ❏ Other (Describe):   Fee: $
❏ Oath/Affirmation   ❏ Acknowledgment   Travel: $

Type of Document   Date of Document   Witness(es) Present   Other Signer(s) Present
                                                        ❏ Yes ❏ No   ❏ Yes ❏ No

Witness: Printed Name   Address/Phone   Signature of Witness

Right Thumbprint of Signer

Comments; Additional Information: If Notarization Failed or Refused, Give Reason:

                                                        ❏ Insufficient ID   ❏ Signer Confused   ❏ Other (Explain in Comments Field)

193

Printed Name of Signer:	Signer's Signature:	Time AM/PM: _____
		Date Notarized: _____

Signer's Complete Address: City   State   Zip   Phone

Identification by: ❏ Identification Card   Issued By: _____   I.D. # _____

❏ Personal Knowledge   ❏ Credible Witness(es)   Type of I.D.: _____   Expiration Date: _____   Date of Birth: _____

Type of Notarial Act: ❏ Verbal Ceremony Performed   ❏ Other (Describe):   Fee: $ Travel: $

❏ Oath/Affirmation   ❏ Acknowledgment

Type of Document   Date of Document   Witness(es) Present ❏ Yes ❏ No   Other Signer(s) Present ❏ Yes ❏ No

Right Thumbprint of Signer

Witness: Printed Name   Address/Phone   Signature of Witness

Comments; Additional Information:

If Notarization Failed or Refused, Give Reason: ❏ Insufficient ID   ❏ Signer Confused   ❏ Other (Explain in Comments Field)

194

Printed Name of Signer:	Signer's Signature:	Time AM/PM: _____
		Date Notarized: _____

Signer's Complete Address: City   State   Zip   Phone

Identification by: ❏ Identification Card   Issued By: _____   I.D. # _____

❏ Personal Knowledge   ❏ Credible Witness(es)   Type of I.D.: _____   Expiration Date: _____   Date of Birth: _____

Type of Notarial Act: ❏ Verbal Ceremony Performed   ❏ Other (Describe):   Fee: $ Travel: $

❏ Oath/Affirmation   ❏ Acknowledgment

Type of Document   Date of Document   Witness(es) Present ❏ Yes ❏ No   Other Signer(s) Present ❏ Yes ❏ No

Right Thumbprint of Signer

Witness: Printed Name   Address/Phone   Signature of Witness

Comments; Additional Information:

If Notarization Failed or Refused, Give Reason: ❏ Insufficient ID   ❏ Signer Confused   ❏ Other (Explain in Comments Field)

195

Printed Name of Signer:	Signer's Signature:	Time AM/PM: _____
		Date Notarized: _____

Signer's Complete Address: City   State   Zip   Phone

Identification by: ❏ Identification Card   Issued By: _____   I.D. # _____

❏ Personal Knowledge   ❏ Credible Witness(es)   Type of I.D.: _____   Expiration Date: _____   Date of Birth: _____

Type of Notarial Act: ❏ Verbal Ceremony Performed   ❏ Other (Describe):   Fee: $ Travel: $

❏ Oath/Affirmation   ❏ Acknowledgment

Type of Document   Date of Document   Witness(es) Present ❏ Yes ❏ No   Other Signer(s) Present ❏ Yes ❏ No

Right Thumbprint of Signer

Witness: Printed Name   Address/Phone   Signature of Witness

Comments; Additional Information:

If Notarization Failed or Refused, Give Reason: ❏ Insufficient ID   ❏ Signer Confused   ❏ Other (Explain in Comments Field)

196

Printed Name of Signer: | Signer's Signature: | Time AM/PM: ____ Date Notarized: ____

Signer's Complete Address: | City | State | Zip | Phone

Identification by: ❑ Identification Card Issued By: ____ I.D. #____

❑ Personal Knowledge ❑ Credible Witness(es) Type of I.D.:____ Expiration Date: ____ Date of Birth: ____

Type of Notarial Act: ❑ Verbal Ceremony Performed ❑ Other (Describe): Fee: $

❑ Oath/Affirmation ❑ Acknowledgment Travel: $

Type of Document | Date of Document | Witness(es) Present ❑ Yes ❑ No | Other Signer(s) Present ❑ Yes ❑ No

Witness: Printed Name | Address/Phone | Signature of Witness

Right Thumbprint of Signer

Comments; Additional Information:

If Notarization Failed or Refused, Give Reason:

❑ Insufficient ID ❑ Signer Confused ❑ Other (Explain in Comments Field)

197

Printed Name of Signer: | Signer's Signature: | Time AM/PM: ____ Date Notarized: ____

Signer's Complete Address: | City | State | Zip | Phone

Identification by: ❑ Identification Card Issued By: ____ I.D. #____

❑ Personal Knowledge ❑ Credible Witness(es) Type of I.D.:____ Expiration Date: ____ Date of Birth: ____

Type of Notarial Act: ❑ Verbal Ceremony Performed ❑ Other (Describe): Fee: $

❑ Oath/Affirmation ❑ Acknowledgment Travel: $

Type of Document | Date of Document | Witness(es) Present ❑ Yes ❑ No | Other Signer(s) Present ❑ Yes ❑ No

Witness: Printed Name | Address/Phone | Signature of Witness

Right Thumbprint of Signer

Comments; Additional Information:

If Notarization Failed or Refused, Give Reason:

❑ Insufficient ID ❑ Signer Confused ❑ Other (Explain in Comments Field)

198

Printed Name of Signer: | Signer's Signature: | Time AM/PM: ____ Date Notarized: ____

Signer's Complete Address: | City | State | Zip | Phone

Identification by: ❑ Identification Card Issued By: ____ I.D. #____

❑ Personal Knowledge ❑ Credible Witness(es) Type of I.D.:____ Expiration Date: ____ Date of Birth: ____

Type of Notarial Act: ❑ Verbal Ceremony Performed ❑ Other (Describe): Fee: $

❑ Oath/Affirmation ❑ Acknowledgment Travel: $

Type of Document | Date of Document | Witness(es) Present ❑ Yes ❑ No | Other Signer(s) Present ❑ Yes ❑ No

Witness: Printed Name | Address/Phone | Signature of Witness

Right Thumbprint of Signer

Comments; Additional Information:

If Notarization Failed or Refused, Give Reason:

❑ Insufficient ID ❑ Signer Confused ❑ Other (Explain in Comments Field)

199

Printed Name of Signer:

Signer's Signature:

Time AM/PM: _____
Date Notarized: _____

Signer's Complete Address:

City

State

Zip

Phone

Identification by:
- ❏ Identification Card
- ❏ Personal Knowledge
- ❏ Credible Witness(es)

Issued By: _____ I.D. # _____

Type of I.D.: _____ Expiration Date: _____ Date of Birth: _____

Type of Notarial Act:
- ❏ Oath/Affirmation
- ❏ Verbal Ceremony Performed
- ❏ Acknowledgment
- ❏ Other (Describe):

Fee: $
Travel: $

Type of Document

Date of Document

Witness(es) Present
❏ Yes ❏ No

Other Signer(s) Present
❏ Yes ❏ No

Right Thumbprint of Signer

Witness: Printed Name

Address/Phone

Signature of Witness

Comments; Additional Information:

If Notarization Failed or Refused, Give Reason:
❏ Insufficient ID ❏ Signer Confused ❏ Other (Explain in Comments Field)

200

Printed Name of Signer:

Signer's Signature:

Time AM/PM: _____
Date Notarized: _____

Signer's Complete Address:

City

State

Zip

Phone

Identification by:
- ❏ Identification Card
- ❏ Personal Knowledge
- ❏ Credible Witness(es)

Issued By: _____ I.D. # _____

Type of I.D.: _____ Expiration Date: _____ Date of Birth: _____

Type of Notarial Act:
- ❏ Oath/Affirmation
- ❏ Verbal Ceremony Performed
- ❏ Acknowledgment
- ❏ Other (Describe):

Fee: $
Travel: $

Type of Document

Date of Document

Witness(es) Present
❏ Yes ❏ No

Other Signer(s) Present
❏ Yes ❏ No

Right Thumbprint of Signer

Witness: Printed Name

Address/Phone

Signature of Witness

Comments; Additional Information:

If Notarization Failed or Refused, Give Reason:
❏ Insufficient ID ❏ Signer Confused ❏ Other (Explain in Comments Field)

201

Printed Name of Signer:

Signer's Signature:

Time AM/PM: _____
Date Notarized: _____

Signer's Complete Address:

City

State

Zip

Phone

Identification by:
- ❏ Identification Card
- ❏ Personal Knowledge
- ❏ Credible Witness(es)

Issued By: _____ I.D. # _____

Type of I.D.: _____ Expiration Date: _____ Date of Birth: _____

Type of Notarial Act:
- ❏ Oath/Affirmation
- ❏ Verbal Ceremony Performed
- ❏ Acknowledgment
- ❏ Other (Describe):

Fee: $
Travel: $

Type of Document

Date of Document

Witness(es) Present
❏ Yes ❏ No

Other Signer(s) Present
❏ Yes ❏ No

Right Thumbprint of Signer

Witness: Printed Name

Address/Phone

Signature of Witness

Comments; Additional Information:

If Notarization Failed or Refused, Give Reason:
❏ Insufficient ID ❏ Signer Confused ❏ Other (Explain in Comments Field)

202

| Printed Name of Signer: | Signer's Signature: | Time AM/PM: _____ |
| | | Date Notarized: _____ |

| Signer's Complete Address: | City | State | Zip | Phone |

Identification by: ❏ Identification Card   Issued By: _____   I.D. # _____

❏ Personal Knowledge   ❏ Credible Witness(es)   Type of I.D.: _____   Expiration Date: _____   Date of Birth: _____

Type of Notarial Act: ❏ Verbal Ceremony Performed   ❏ Other (Describe):   Fee: $
❏ Oath/Affirmation   ❏ Acknowledgment   Travel: $

Type of Document   Date of Document   Witness(es) Present   Other Signer(s) Present

❏ Yes ❏ No   ❏ Yes ❏ No

Witness: Printed Name   Address/Phone   Signature of Witness

Right Thumbprint of Signer

Comments; Additional Information:

If Notarization Failed or Refused, Give Reason:

❏ Insufficient ID   ❏ Signer Confused   ❏ Other (Explain in Comments Field)

203

| Printed Name of Signer: | Signer's Signature: | Time AM/PM: _____ |
| | | Date Notarized: _____ |

| Signer's Complete Address: | City | State | Zip | Phone |

Identification by: ❏ Identification Card   Issued By: _____   I.D. # _____

❏ Personal Knowledge   ❏ Credible Witness(es)   Type of I.D.: _____   Expiration Date: _____   Date of Birth: _____

Type of Notarial Act: ❏ Verbal Ceremony Performed   ❏ Other (Describe):   Fee: $
❏ Oath/Affirmation   ❏ Acknowledgment   Travel: $

Type of Document   Date of Document   Witness(es) Present   Other Signer(s) Present

❏ Yes ❏ No   ❏ Yes ❏ No

Witness: Printed Name   Address/Phone   Signature of Witness

Right Thumbprint of Signer

Comments; Additional Information:

If Notarization Failed or Refused, Give Reason:

❏ Insufficient ID   ❏ Signer Confused   ❏ Other (Explain in Comments Field)

204

| Printed Name of Signer: | Signer's Signature: | Time AM/PM: _____ |
| | | Date Notarized: _____ |

| Signer's Complete Address: | City | State | Zip | Phone |

Identification by: ❏ Identification Card   Issued By: _____   I.D. # _____

❏ Personal Knowledge   ❏ Credible Witness(es)   Type of I.D.: _____   Expiration Date: _____   Date of Birth: _____

Type of Notarial Act: ❏ Verbal Ceremony Performed   ❏ Other (Describe):   Fee: $
❏ Oath/Affirmation   ❏ Acknowledgment   Travel: $

Type of Document   Date of Document   Witness(es) Present   Other Signer(s) Present

❏ Yes ❏ No   ❏ Yes ❏ No

Witness: Printed Name   Address/Phone   Signature of Witness

Right Thumbprint of Signer

Comments; Additional Information:

If Notarization Failed or Refused, Give Reason:

❏ Insufficient ID   ❏ Signer Confused   ❏ Other (Explain in Comments Field)

205

| Printed Name of Signer: | Signer's Signature: | Time AM/PM: _____ |
| | | Date Notarized: _____ |

| Signer's Complete Address: | City | State | Zip | Phone |

Identification by: ❏ Identification Card Issued By: _____ I.D. # _____

❏ Personal Knowledge ❏ Credible Witness(es) Type of I.D.: _____ Expiration Date: _____ Date of Birth: _____

Type of Notarial Act: ❏ Verbal Ceremony Performed ❏ Other (Describe): _____ Fee: $ _____ Travel: $ _____

❏ Oath/Affirmation ❏ Acknowledgment

| Type of Document | Date of Document | Witness(es) Present ❏ Yes ❏ No | Other Signer(s) Present ❏ Yes ❏ No | Right Thumbprint of Signer |

Witness: Printed Name Address/Phone Signature of Witness

Comments; Additional Information:

If Notarization Failed or Refused, Give Reason:
❏ Insufficient ID ❏ Signer Confused ❏ Other (Explain in Comments Field)

206

| Printed Name of Signer: | Signer's Signature: | Time AM/PM: _____ |
| | | Date Notarized: _____ |

| Signer's Complete Address: | City | State | Zip | Phone |

Identification by: ❏ Identification Card Issued By: _____ I.D. # _____

❏ Personal Knowledge ❏ Credible Witness(es) Type of I.D.: _____ Expiration Date: _____ Date of Birth: _____

Type of Notarial Act: ❏ Verbal Ceremony Performed ❏ Other (Describe): _____ Fee: $ _____ Travel: $ _____

❏ Oath/Affirmation ❏ Acknowledgment

| Type of Document | Date of Document | Witness(es) Present ❏ Yes ❏ No | Other Signer(s) Present ❏ Yes ❏ No | Right Thumbprint of Signer |

Witness: Printed Name Address/Phone Signature of Witness

Comments; Additional Information:

If Notarization Failed or Refused, Give Reason:
❏ Insufficient ID ❏ Signer Confused ❏ Other (Explain in Comments Field)

207

| Printed Name of Signer: | Signer's Signature: | Time AM/PM: _____ |
| | | Date Notarized: _____ |

| Signer's Complete Address: | City | State | Zip | Phone |

Identification by: ❏ Identification Card Issued By: _____ I.D. # _____

❏ Personal Knowledge ❏ Credible Witness(es) Type of I.D.: _____ Expiration Date: _____ Date of Birth: _____

Type of Notarial Act: ❏ Verbal Ceremony Performed ❏ Other (Describe): _____ Fee: $ _____ Travel: $ _____

❏ Oath/Affirmation ❏ Acknowledgment

| Type of Document | Date of Document | Witness(es) Present ❏ Yes ❏ No | Other Signer(s) Present ❏ Yes ❏ No | Right Thumbprint of Signer |

Witness: Printed Name Address/Phone Signature of Witness

Comments; Additional Information:

If Notarization Failed or Refused, Give Reason:
❏ Insufficient ID ❏ Signer Confused ❏ Other (Explain in Comments Field)

208

| Printed Name of Signer: | Signer's Signature: | Time AM/PM: _____ |
| | | Date Notarized: _____ |

Signer's Complete Address: City   State   Zip   Phone

Identification by: ❑ Identification Card   Issued By: _____   I.D. # _____

❑ Personal Knowledge   ❑ Credible Witness(es)   Type of I.D.: _____   Expiration Date: _____   Date of Birth: _____

| Type of Notarial Act: | ❑ Verbal Ceremony Performed | ❑ Other (Describe): | Fee: $ | Right Thumbprint of Signer |
| ❑ Oath/Affirmation | ❑ Acknowledgment | | Travel: $ | |

| Type of Document | Date of Document | Witness(es) Present ❑ Yes ❑ No | Other Signer(s) Present ❑ Yes ❑ No | |

| Witness: Printed Name | Address/Phone | Signature of Witness | |

Comments; Additional Information: If Notarization Failed or Refused, Give Reason:

❑ Insufficient ID   ❑ Signer Confused   ❑ Other (Explain in Comments Field)

209

| Printed Name of Signer: | Signer's Signature: | Time AM/PM: _____ |
| | | Date Notarized: _____ |

Signer's Complete Address: City   State   Zip   Phone

Identification by: ❑ Identification Card   Issued By: _____   I.D. # _____

❑ Personal Knowledge   ❑ Credible Witness(es)   Type of I.D.: _____   Expiration Date: _____   Date of Birth: _____

| Type of Notarial Act: | ❑ Verbal Ceremony Performed | ❑ Other (Describe): | Fee: $ | Right Thumbprint of Signer |
| ❑ Oath/Affirmation | ❑ Acknowledgment | | Travel: $ | |

| Type of Document | Date of Document | Witness(es) Present ❑ Yes ❑ No | Other Signer(s) Present ❑ Yes ❑ No | |

| Witness: Printed Name | Address/Phone | Signature of Witness | |

Comments; Additional Information: If Notarization Failed or Refused, Give Reason:

❑ Insufficient ID   ❑ Signer Confused   ❑ Other (Explain in Comments Field)

210

| Printed Name of Signer: | Signer's Signature: | Time AM/PM: _____ |
| | | Date Notarized: _____ |

Signer's Complete Address: City   State   Zip   Phone

Identification by: ❑ Identification Card   Issued By: _____   I.D. # _____

❑ Personal Knowledge   ❑ Credible Witness(es)   Type of I.D.: _____   Expiration Date: _____   Date of Birth: _____

| Type of Notarial Act: | ❑ Verbal Ceremony Performed | ❑ Other (Describe): | Fee: $ | Right Thumbprint of Signer |
| ❑ Oath/Affirmation | ❑ Acknowledgment | | Travel: $ | |

| Type of Document | Date of Document | Witness(es) Present ❑ Yes ❑ No | Other Signer(s) Present ❑ Yes ❑ No | |

| Witness: Printed Name | Address/Phone | Signature of Witness | |

Comments; Additional Information: If Notarization Failed or Refused, Give Reason:

❑ Insufficient ID   ❑ Signer Confused   ❑ Other (Explain in Comments Field)

211

| Printed Name of Signer: | Signer's Signature: | Time AM/PM: _____ |
| | | Date Notarized: _____ |

| Signer's Complete Address: | City | State | Zip | Phone |

Identification by: ❏ Identification Card   Issued By: _____   I.D. # _____

❏ Personal Knowledge   ❏ Credible Witness(es)   Type of I.D.: _____   Expiration Date: _____   Date of Birth: _____

| Type of Notarial Act: | ❏ Verbal Ceremony Performed | ❏ Other (Describe): | Fee: $ | |
| ❏ Oath/Affirmation | ❏ Acknowledgment | | Travel: $ | |

| Type of Document | Date of Document | Witness(es) Present ❏ Yes ❏ No | Other Signer(s) Present ❏ Yes ❏ No | Right Thumbprint of Signer |

| Witness: Printed Name | Address/Phone | Signature of Witness |

Comments; Additional Information:

If Notarization Failed or Refused, Give Reason:

❏ Insufficient ID   ❏ Signer Confused   ❏ Other (Explain in Comments Field)

212

| Printed Name of Signer: | Signer's Signature: | Time AM/PM: _____ |
| | | Date Notarized: _____ |

| Signer's Complete Address: | City | State | Zip | Phone |

Identification by: ❏ Identification Card   Issued By: _____   I.D. # _____

❏ Personal Knowledge   ❏ Credible Witness(es)   Type of I.D.: _____   Expiration Date: _____   Date of Birth: _____

| Type of Notarial Act: | ❏ Verbal Ceremony Performed | ❏ Other (Describe): | Fee: $ | |
| ❏ Oath/Affirmation | ❏ Acknowledgment | | Travel: $ | |

| Type of Document | Date of Document | Witness(es) Present ❏ Yes ❏ No | Other Signer(s) Present ❏ Yes ❏ No | Right Thumbprint of Signer |

| Witness: Printed Name | Address/Phone | Signature of Witness |

Comments; Additional Information:

If Notarization Failed or Refused, Give Reason:

❏ Insufficient ID   ❏ Signer Confused   ❏ Other (Explain in Comments Field)

213

| Printed Name of Signer: | Signer's Signature: | Time AM/PM: _____ |
| | | Date Notarized: _____ |

| Signer's Complete Address: | City | State | Zip | Phone |

Identification by: ❏ Identification Card   Issued By: _____   I.D. # _____

❏ Personal Knowledge   ❏ Credible Witness(es)   Type of I.D.: _____   Expiration Date: _____   Date of Birth: _____

| Type of Notarial Act: | ❏ Verbal Ceremony Performed | ❏ Other (Describe): | Fee: $ | |
| ❏ Oath/Affirmation | ❏ Acknowledgment | | Travel: $ | |

| Type of Document | Date of Document | Witness(es) Present ❏ Yes ❏ No | Other Signer(s) Present ❏ Yes ❏ No | Right Thumbprint of Signer |

| Witness: Printed Name | Address/Phone | Signature of Witness |

Comments; Additional Information:

If Notarization Failed or Refused, Give Reason:

❏ Insufficient ID   ❏ Signer Confused   ❏ Other (Explain in Comments Field)

Printed Name of Signer:

Signer's Signature:

Time AM/PM: _____

Date Notarized: _____

214

Signer's Complete Address: City State Zip Phone

Identification by: ❏ Identification Card Issued By: _____ I.D. # _____

❏ Personal Knowledge ❏ Credible Witness(es) Type of I.D.: _____ Expiration Date: _____ Date of Birth: _____

Type of Notarial Act: ❏ Verbal Ceremony Performed ❏ Other (Describe): Fee: $

❏ Oath/Affirmation ❏ Acknowledgment Travel: $

Type of Document Date of Document Witness(es) Present Other Signer(s) Present

❏ Yes ❏ No ❏ Yes ❏ No

Right Thumbprint of Signer

Witness: Printed Name Address/Phone Signature of Witness

Comments; Additional Information:

If Notarization Failed or Refused, Give Reason:

❏ Insufficient ID ❏ Signer Confused ❏ Other (Explain in Comments Field)

Printed Name of Signer:

Signer's Signature:

Time AM/PM: _____

Date Notarized: _____

215

Signer's Complete Address: City State Zip Phone

Identification by: ❏ Identification Card Issued By: _____ I.D. # _____

❏ Personal Knowledge ❏ Credible Witness(es) Type of I.D.: _____ Expiration Date: _____ Date of Birth: _____

Type of Notarial Act: ❏ Verbal Ceremony Performed ❏ Other (Describe): Fee: $

❏ Oath/Affirmation ❏ Acknowledgment Travel: $

Type of Document Date of Document Witness(es) Present Other Signer(s) Present

❏ Yes ❏ No ❏ Yes ❏ No

Right Thumbprint of Signer

Witness: Printed Name Address/Phone Signature of Witness

Comments; Additional Information:

If Notarization Failed or Refused, Give Reason:

❏ Insufficient ID ❏ Signer Confused ❏ Other (Explain in Comments Field)

Printed Name of Signer:

Signer's Signature:

Time AM/PM: _____

Date Notarized: _____

216

Signer's Complete Address: City State Zip Phone

Identification by: ❏ Identification Card Issued By: _____ I.D. # _____

❏ Personal Knowledge ❏ Credible Witness(es) Type of I.D.: _____ Expiration Date: _____ Date of Birth: _____

Type of Notarial Act: ❏ Verbal Ceremony Performed ❏ Other (Describe): Fee: $

❏ Oath/Affirmation ❏ Acknowledgment Travel: $

Type of Document Date of Document Witness(es) Present Other Signer(s) Present

❏ Yes ❏ No ❏ Yes ❏ No

Right Thumbprint of Signer

Witness: Printed Name Address/Phone Signature of Witness

Comments; Additional Information:

If Notarization Failed or Refused, Give Reason:

❏ Insufficient ID ❏ Signer Confused ❏ Other (Explain in Comments Field)

217

Printed Name of Signer:

Signer's Signature:

Time AM/PM: _____
Date Notarized: _____

Signer's Complete Address:

City

State   Zip   Phone

Identification by: ❏ Identification Card   Issued By: _____   I.D. # _____

❏ Personal Knowledge   ❏ Credible Witness(es)   Type of I.D.: _____   Expiration Date: _____   Date of Birth: _____

Type of Notarial Act: ❏ Verbal Ceremony Performed   ❏ Other (Describe):   Fee: $

❏ Oath/Affirmation   ❏ Acknowledgment   Travel: $

Type of Document   Date of Document   Witness(es) Present   Other Signer(s) Present

❏ Yes ❏ No   ❏ Yes ❏ No

Witness: Printed Name   Address/Phone   Signature of Witness

Right Thumbprint of Signer

Comments; Additional Information:

If Notarization Failed or Refused, Give Reason:

❏ Insufficient ID   ❏ Signer Confused   ❏ Other (Explain in Comments Field)

218

Printed Name of Signer:

Signer's Signature:

Time AM/PM: _____
Date Notarized: _____

Signer's Complete Address:

City

State   Zip   Phone

Identification by: ❏ Identification Card   Issued By: _____   I.D. # _____

❏ Personal Knowledge   ❏ Credible Witness(es)   Type of I.D.: _____   Expiration Date: _____   Date of Birth: _____

Type of Notarial Act: ❏ Verbal Ceremony Performed   ❏ Other (Describe):   Fee: $

❏ Oath/Affirmation   ❏ Acknowledgment   Travel: $

Type of Document   Date of Document   Witness(es) Present   Other Signer(s) Present

❏ Yes ❏ No   ❏ Yes ❏ No

Witness: Printed Name   Address/Phone   Signature of Witness

Right Thumbprint of Signer

Comments; Additional Information:

If Notarization Failed or Refused, Give Reason:

❏ Insufficient ID   ❏ Signer Confused   ❏ Other (Explain in Comments Field)

219

Printed Name of Signer:

Signer's Signature:

Time AM/PM: _____
Date Notarized: _____

Signer's Complete Address:

City

State   Zip   Phone

Identification by: ❏ Identification Card   Issued By: _____   I.D. # _____

❏ Personal Knowledge   ❏ Credible Witness(es)   Type of I.D.: _____   Expiration Date: _____   Date of Birth: _____

Type of Notarial Act: ❏ Verbal Ceremony Performed   ❏ Other (Describe):   Fee: $

❏ Oath/Affirmation   ❏ Acknowledgment   Travel: $

Type of Document   Date of Document   Witness(es) Present   Other Signer(s) Present

❏ Yes ❏ No   ❏ Yes ❏ No

Witness: Printed Name   Address/Phone   Signature of Witness

Right Thumbprint of Signer

Comments; Additional Information:

If Notarization Failed or Refused, Give Reason:

❏ Insufficient ID   ❏ Signer Confused   ❏ Other (Explain in Comments Field)

220

Printed Name of Signer:

Signer's Signature:

Time AM/PM: _____

Date Notarized: _____

Signer's Complete Address: City   State   Zip   Phone

Identification by: ❏ Identification Card   Issued By: _____   I.D. # _____

❏ Personal Knowledge   ❏ Credible Witness(es)   Type of I.D.: _____   Expiration Date: _____   Date of Birth: _____

Type of Notarial Act: ❏ Verbal Ceremony Performed   ❏ Other (Describe):   Fee: $

❏ Oath/Affirmation   ❏ Acknowledgment   Travel: $

Type of Document   Date of Document   Witness(es) Present   Other Signer(s) Present

❏ Yes ❏ No   ❏ Yes ❏ No

Witness: Printed Name   Address/Phone   Signature of Witness

Right Thumbprint of Signer

Comments; Additional Information: If Notarization Failed or Refused, Give Reason:

❏ Insufficient ID   ❏ Signer Confused   ❏ Other (Explain in Comments Field)

221

Printed Name of Signer:

Signer's Signature:

Time AM/PM: _____

Date Notarized: _____

Signer's Complete Address: City   State   Zip   Phone

Identification by: ❏ Identification Card   Issued By: _____   I.D. # _____

❏ Personal Knowledge   ❏ Credible Witness(es)   Type of I.D.: _____   Expiration Date: _____   Date of Birth: _____

Type of Notarial Act: ❏ Verbal Ceremony Performed   ❏ Other (Describe):   Fee: $

❏ Oath/Affirmation   ❏ Acknowledgment   Travel: $

Type of Document   Date of Document   Witness(es) Present   Other Signer(s) Present

❏ Yes ❏ No   ❏ Yes ❏ No

Witness: Printed Name   Address/Phone   Signature of Witness

Right Thumbprint of Signer

Comments; Additional Information: If Notarization Failed or Refused, Give Reason:

❏ Insufficient ID   ❏ Signer Confused   ❏ Other (Explain in Comments Field)

222

Printed Name of Signer:

Signer's Signature:

Time AM/PM: _____

Date Notarized: _____

Signer's Complete Address: City   State   Zip   Phone

Identification by: ❏ Identification Card   Issued By: _____   I.D. # _____

❏ Personal Knowledge   ❏ Credible Witness(es)   Type of I.D.: _____   Expiration Date: _____   Date of Birth: _____

Type of Notarial Act: ❏ Verbal Ceremony Performed   ❏ Other (Describe):   Fee: $

❏ Oath/Affirmation   ❏ Acknowledgment   Travel: $

Type of Document   Date of Document   Witness(es) Present   Other Signer(s) Present

❏ Yes ❏ No   ❏ Yes ❏ No

Witness: Printed Name   Address/Phone   Signature of Witness

Right Thumbprint of Signer

Comments; Additional Information: If Notarization Failed or Refused, Give Reason:

❏ Insufficient ID   ❏ Signer Confused   ❏ Other (Explain in Comments Field)

223

Printed Name of Signer:

Signer's Signature:

Time AM/PM: _____
Date Notarized: _____

Signer's Complete Address: City   State   Zip   Phone

Identification by: ❏ Identification Card   Issued By: _____   I.D. # _____

❏ Personal Knowledge   ❏ Credible Witness(es)   Type of I.D.: _____   Expiration Date: _____   Date of Birth: _____

Type of Notarial Act: ❏ Verbal Ceremony Performed   ❏ Other (Describe):   Fee: $ _____

❏ Oath/Affirmation   ❏ Acknowledgment   Travel: $ _____

Type of Document   Date of Document   Witness(es) Present   Other Signer(s) Present
                                                ❏ Yes ❏ No   ❏ Yes ❏ No

Witness: Printed Name   Address/Phone   Signature of Witness

Right Thumbprint of Signer

Comments; Additional Information: If Notarization Failed or Refused, Give Reason:

❏ Insufficient ID   ❏ Signer Confused   ❏ Other (Explain in Comments Field)

224

Printed Name of Signer:

Signer's Signature:

Time AM/PM: _____
Date Notarized: _____

Signer's Complete Address: City   State   Zip   Phone

Identification by: ❏ Identification Card   Issued By: _____   I.D. # _____

❏ Personal Knowledge   ❏ Credible Witness(es)   Type of I.D.: _____   Expiration Date: _____   Date of Birth: _____

Type of Notarial Act: ❏ Verbal Ceremony Performed   ❏ Other (Describe):   Fee: $ _____

❏ Oath/Affirmation   ❏ Acknowledgment   Travel: $ _____

Type of Document   Date of Document   Witness(es) Present   Other Signer(s) Present
                                                ❏ Yes ❏ No   ❏ Yes ❏ No

Witness: Printed Name   Address/Phone   Signature of Witness

Right Thumbprint of Signer

Comments; Additional Information: If Notarization Failed or Refused, Give Reason:

❏ Insufficient ID   ❏ Signer Confused   ❏ Other (Explain in Comments Field)

225

Printed Name of Signer:

Signer's Signature:

Time AM/PM: _____
Date Notarized: _____

Signer's Complete Address: City   State   Zip   Phone

Identification by: ❏ Identification Card   Issued By: _____   I.D. # _____

❏ Personal Knowledge   ❏ Credible Witness(es)   Type of I.D.: _____   Expiration Date: _____   Date of Birth: _____

Type of Notarial Act: ❏ Verbal Ceremony Performed   ❏ Other (Describe):   Fee: $ _____

❏ Oath/Affirmation   ❏ Acknowledgment   Travel: $ _____

Type of Document   Date of Document   Witness(es) Present   Other Signer(s) Present
                                                ❏ Yes ❏ No   ❏ Yes ❏ No

Witness: Printed Name   Address/Phone   Signature of Witness

Right Thumbprint of Signer

Comments; Additional Information: If Notarization Failed or Refused, Give Reason:

❏ Insufficient ID   ❏ Signer Confused   ❏ Other (Explain in Comments Field)

226

| Printed Name of Signer: | Signer's Signature: | Time AM/PM: _____ |
| | | Date Notarized: _____ |

| Signer's Complete Address: | City | State | Zip | Phone |

Identification by: ❏ Identification Card   Issued By: _____   I.D. # _____

❏ Personal Knowledge   ❏ Credible Witness(es)   Type of I.D.: _____   Expiration Date: _____   Date of Birth: _____

| Type of Notarial Act: ❏ Verbal Ceremony Performed | ❏ Other (Describe): | Fee: $ | |
| ❏ Oath/Affirmation   ❏ Acknowledgment | | Travel: $ | Right Thumbprint of Signer |

| Type of Document | Date of Document | Witness(es) Present ❏ Yes ❏ No | Other Signer(s) Present ❏ Yes ❏ No | |

| Witness: Printed Name | Address/Phone | Signature of Witness | |

Comments; Additional Information:

If Notarization Failed or Refused, Give Reason:

❏ Insufficient ID   ❏ Signer Confused   ❏ Other (Explain in Comments Field)

227

| Printed Name of Signer: | Signer's Signature: | Time AM/PM: _____ |
| | | Date Notarized: _____ |

| Signer's Complete Address: | City | State | Zip | Phone |

Identification by: ❏ Identification Card   Issued By: _____   I.D. # _____

❏ Personal Knowledge   ❏ Credible Witness(es)   Type of I.D.: _____   Expiration Date: _____   Date of Birth: _____

| Type of Notarial Act: ❏ Verbal Ceremony Performed | ❏ Other (Describe): | Fee: $ | |
| ❏ Oath/Affirmation   ❏ Acknowledgment | | Travel: $ | Right Thumbprint of Signer |

| Type of Document | Date of Document | Witness(es) Present ❏ Yes ❏ No | Other Signer(s) Present ❏ Yes ❏ No | |

| Witness: Printed Name | Address/Phone | Signature of Witness | |

Comments; Additional Information:

If Notarization Failed or Refused, Give Reason:

❏ Insufficient ID   ❏ Signer Confused   ❏ Other (Explain in Comments Field)

228

| Printed Name of Signer: | Signer's Signature: | Time AM/PM: _____ |
| | | Date Notarized: _____ |

| Signer's Complete Address: | City | State | Zip | Phone |

Identification by: ❏ Identification Card   Issued By: _____   I.D. # _____

❏ Personal Knowledge   ❏ Credible Witness(es)   Type of I.D.: _____   Expiration Date: _____   Date of Birth: _____

| Type of Notarial Act: ❏ Verbal Ceremony Performed | ❏ Other (Describe): | Fee: $ | |
| ❏ Oath/Affirmation   ❏ Acknowledgment | | Travel: $ | Right Thumbprint of Signer |

| Type of Document | Date of Document | Witness(es) Present ❏ Yes ❏ No | Other Signer(s) Present ❏ Yes ❏ No | |

| Witness: Printed Name | Address/Phone | Signature of Witness | |

Comments; Additional Information:

If Notarization Failed or Refused, Give Reason:

❏ Insufficient ID   ❏ Signer Confused   ❏ Other (Explain in Comments Field)

229

| Printed Name of Signer: | Signer's Signature: | Time AM/PM: _____ |
| | | Date Notarized: _____ |

Signer's Complete Address: City   State   Zip   Phone

Identification by: ❑ Identification Card   Issued By: _____   I.D. # _____

❑ Personal Knowledge   ❑ Credible Witness(es)   Type of I.D.: _____ Expiration Date: _____ Date of Birth: _____

Type of Notarial Act: ❑ Verbal Ceremony Performed   ❑ Other (Describe):   Fee: $

❑ Oath/Affirmation   ❑ Acknowledgment   Travel: $

Type of Document   Date of Document   Witness(es) Present   Other Signer(s) Present

❑ Yes ❑ No   ❑ Yes ❑ No

Witness: Printed Name   Address/Phone   Signature of Witness

Right Thumbprint of Signer

Comments; Additional Information: If Notarization Failed or Refused, Give Reason:

❑ Insufficient ID   ❑ Signer Confused   ❑ Other (Explain in Comments Field)

230

| Printed Name of Signer: | Signer's Signature: | Time AM/PM: _____ |
| | | Date Notarized: _____ |

Signer's Complete Address: City   State   Zip   Phone

Identification by: ❑ Identification Card   Issued By: _____   I.D. # _____

❑ Personal Knowledge   ❑ Credible Witness(es)   Type of I.D.: _____ Expiration Date: _____ Date of Birth: _____

Type of Notarial Act: ❑ Verbal Ceremony Performed   ❑ Other (Describe):   Fee: $

❑ Oath/Affirmation   ❑ Acknowledgment   Travel: $

Type of Document   Date of Document   Witness(es) Present   Other Signer(s) Present

❑ Yes ❑ No   ❑ Yes ❑ No

Witness: Printed Name   Address/Phone   Signature of Witness

Right Thumbprint of Signer

Comments; Additional Information: If Notarization Failed or Refused, Give Reason:

❑ Insufficient ID   ❑ Signer Confused   ❑ Other (Explain in Comments Field)

231

| Printed Name of Signer: | Signer's Signature: | Time AM/PM: _____ |
| | | Date Notarized: _____ |

Signer's Complete Address: City   State   Zip   Phone

Identification by: ❑ Identification Card   Issued By: _____   I.D. # _____

❑ Personal Knowledge   ❑ Credible Witness(es)   Type of I.D.: _____ Expiration Date: _____ Date of Birth: _____

Type of Notarial Act: ❑ Verbal Ceremony Performed   ❑ Other (Describe):   Fee: $

❑ Oath/Affirmation   ❑ Acknowledgment   Travel: $

Type of Document   Date of Document   Witness(es) Present   Other Signer(s) Present

❑ Yes ❑ No   ❑ Yes ❑ No

Witness: Printed Name   Address/Phone   Signature of Witness

Right Thumbprint of Signer

Comments; Additional Information: If Notarization Failed or Refused, Give Reason:

❑ Insufficient ID   ❑ Signer Confused   ❑ Other (Explain in Comments Field)

232

| Printed Name of Signer: | Signer's Signature: | Time AM/PM: _____ |
| | | Date Notarized: _____ |

Signer's Complete Address: City   State   Zip   Phone

Identification by: ❏ Identification Card   Issued By: _____   I.D. # _____

❏ Personal Knowledge   ❏ Credible Witness(es)   Type of I.D.: _____   Expiration Date: _____   Date of Birth: _____

| Type of Notarial Act: | ❏ Verbal Ceremony Performed | ❏ Other (Describe): | Fee: $ | |
| ❏ Oath/Affirmation | ❏ Acknowledgment | | Travel: $ | Right Thumbprint of Signer |

Type of Document   Date of Document   Witness(es) Present   Other Signer(s) Present
                                            ❏ Yes ❏ No   ❏ Yes ❏ No

Witness: Printed Name   Address/Phone   Signature of Witness

Comments; Additional Information: If Notarization Failed or Refused, Give Reason:

❏ Insufficient ID   ❏ Signer Confused   ❏ Other (Explain in Comments Field)

233

| Printed Name of Signer: | Signer's Signature: | Time AM/PM: _____ |
| | | Date Notarized: _____ |

Signer's Complete Address: City   State   Zip   Phone

Identification by: ❏ Identification Card   Issued By: _____   I.D. # _____

❏ Personal Knowledge   ❏ Credible Witness(es)   Type of I.D.: _____   Expiration Date: _____   Date of Birth: _____

| Type of Notarial Act: | ❏ Verbal Ceremony Performed | ❏ Other (Describe): | Fee: $ | |
| ❏ Oath/Affirmation | ❏ Acknowledgment | | Travel: $ | Right Thumbprint of Signer |

Type of Document   Date of Document   Witness(es) Present   Other Signer(s) Present
                                            ❏ Yes ❏ No   ❏ Yes ❏ No

Witness: Printed Name   Address/Phone   Signature of Witness

Comments; Additional Information: If Notarization Failed or Refused, Give Reason:

❏ Insufficient ID   ❏ Signer Confused   ❏ Other (Explain in Comments Field)

234

| Printed Name of Signer: | Signer's Signature: | Time AM/PM: _____ |
| | | Date Notarized: _____ |

Signer's Complete Address: City   State   Zip   Phone

Identification by: ❏ Identification Card   Issued By: _____   I.D. # _____

❏ Personal Knowledge   ❏ Credible Witness(es)   Type of I.D.: _____   Expiration Date: _____   Date of Birth: _____

| Type of Notarial Act: | ❏ Verbal Ceremony Performed | ❏ Other (Describe): | Fee: $ | |
| ❏ Oath/Affirmation | ❏ Acknowledgment | | Travel: $ | Right Thumbprint of Signer |

Type of Document   Date of Document   Witness(es) Present   Other Signer(s) Present
                                            ❏ Yes ❏ No   ❏ Yes ❏ No

Witness: Printed Name   Address/Phone   Signature of Witness

Comments; Additional Information: If Notarization Failed or Refused, Give Reason:

❏ Insufficient ID   ❏ Signer Confused   ❏ Other (Explain in Comments Field)

235

| Printed Name of Signer: | Signer's Signature: | Time AM/PM: _____ |
| | | Date Notarized: _____ |

| Signer's Complete Address: | City | State | Zip | Phone |

Identification by: ❑ Identification Card Issued By: _____ I.D. # _____

❑ Personal Knowledge ❑ Credible Witness(es) Type of I.D.: _____ Expiration Date: _____ Date of Birth: _____

Type of Notarial Act: ❑ Verbal Ceremony Performed ❑ Other (Describe):   Fee: $

❑ Oath/Affirmation ❑ Acknowledgment   Travel: $

Type of Document   Date of Document Witness(es) Present Other Signer(s) Present

❑ Yes ❑ No   ❑ Yes ❑ No

Witness: Printed Name   Address/Phone   Signature of Witness

Right Thumbprint of Signer

Comments; Additional Information: If Notarization Failed or Refused, Give Reason:

❑ Insufficient ID ❑ Signer Confused ❑ Other (Explain in Comments Field)

236

| Printed Name of Signer: | Signer's Signature: | Time AM/PM: _____ |
| | | Date Notarized: _____ |

| Signer's Complete Address: | City | State | Zip | Phone |

Identification by: ❑ Identification Card Issued By: _____ I.D. # _____

❑ Personal Knowledge ❑ Credible Witness(es) Type of I.D.: _____ Expiration Date: _____ Date of Birth: _____

Type of Notarial Act: ❑ Verbal Ceremony Performed ❑ Other (Describe):   Fee: $

❑ Oath/Affirmation ❑ Acknowledgment   Travel: $

Type of Document   Date of Document Witness(es) Present Other Signer(s) Present

❑ Yes ❑ No   ❑ Yes ❑ No

Witness: Printed Name   Address/Phone   Signature of Witness

Right Thumbprint of Signer

Comments; Additional Information: If Notarization Failed or Refused, Give Reason:

❑ Insufficient ID ❑ Signer Confused ❑ Other (Explain in Comments Field)

237

| Printed Name of Signer: | Signer's Signature: | Time AM/PM: _____ |
| | | Date Notarized: _____ |

| Signer's Complete Address: | City | State | Zip | Phone |

Identification by: ❑ Identification Card Issued By: _____ I.D. # _____

❑ Personal Knowledge ❑ Credible Witness(es) Type of I.D.: _____ Expiration Date: _____ Date of Birth: _____

Type of Notarial Act: ❑ Verbal Ceremony Performed ❑ Other (Describe):   Fee: $

❑ Oath/Affirmation ❑ Acknowledgment   Travel: $

Type of Document   Date of Document Witness(es) Present Other Signer(s) Present

❑ Yes ❑ No   ❑ Yes ❑ No

Witness: Printed Name   Address/Phone   Signature of Witness

Right Thumbprint of Signer

Comments; Additional Information: If Notarization Failed or Refused, Give Reason:

❑ Insufficient ID ❑ Signer Confused ❑ Other (Explain in Comments Field)

238

| Printed Name of Signer: | Signer's Signature: | Time AM/PM: _____ |
| | | Date Notarized: _____ |

Signer's Complete Address: | City | State | Zip | Phone

Identification by: ❑ Identification Card | Issued By: _____ | I.D. # _____

❑ Personal Knowledge ❑ Credible Witness(es) | Type of I.D.: _____ | Expiration Date: _____ | Date of Birth: _____

Type of Notarial Act: ❑ Verbal Ceremony Performed | ❑ Other (Describe): | Fee: $
❑ Oath/Affirmation ❑ Acknowledgment | | Travel: $

Type of Document | Date of Document | Witness(es) Present ❑ Yes ❑ No | Other Signer(s) Present ❑ Yes ❑ No | Right Thumbprint of Signer

Witness: Printed Name | Address/Phone | Signature of Witness

Comments; Additional Information: | If Notarization Failed or Refused, Give Reason:
❑ Insufficient ID ❑ Signer Confused ❑ Other (Explain in Comments Field)

239

| Printed Name of Signer: | Signer's Signature: | Time AM/PM: _____ |
| | | Date Notarized: _____ |

Signer's Complete Address: | City | State | Zip | Phone

Identification by: ❑ Identification Card | Issued By: _____ | I.D. # _____

❑ Personal Knowledge ❑ Credible Witness(es) | Type of I.D.: _____ | Expiration Date: _____ | Date of Birth: _____

Type of Notarial Act: ❑ Verbal Ceremony Performed | ❑ Other (Describe): | Fee: $
❑ Oath/Affirmation ❑ Acknowledgment | | Travel: $

Type of Document | Date of Document | Witness(es) Present ❑ Yes ❑ No | Other Signer(s) Present ❑ Yes ❑ No | Right Thumbprint of Signer

Witness: Printed Name | Address/Phone | Signature of Witness

Comments; Additional Information: | If Notarization Failed or Refused, Give Reason:
❑ Insufficient ID ❑ Signer Confused ❑ Other (Explain in Comments Field)

240

| Printed Name of Signer: | Signer's Signature: | Time AM/PM: _____ |
| | | Date Notarized: _____ |

Signer's Complete Address: | City | State | Zip | Phone

Identification by: ❑ Identification Card | Issued By: _____ | I.D. # _____

❑ Personal Knowledge ❑ Credible Witness(es) | Type of I.D.: _____ | Expiration Date: _____ | Date of Birth: _____

Type of Notarial Act: ❑ Verbal Ceremony Performed | ❑ Other (Describe): | Fee: $
❑ Oath/Affirmation ❑ Acknowledgment | | Travel: $

Type of Document | Date of Document | Witness(es) Present ❑ Yes ❑ No | Other Signer(s) Present ❑ Yes ❑ No | Right Thumbprint of Signer

Witness: Printed Name | Address/Phone | Signature of Witness

Comments; Additional Information: | If Notarization Failed or Refused, Give Reason:
❑ Insufficient ID ❑ Signer Confused ❑ Other (Explain in Comments Field)

241

| Printed Name of Signer: | Signer's Signature: | Time AM/PM: _____ |
| | | Date Notarized: _____ |

| Signer's Complete Address: | City | State | Zip | Phone |

Identification by: ❑ Identification Card   Issued By: _____   I.D. # _____

❑ Personal Knowledge   ❑ Credible Witness(es)   Type of I.D.: _____   Expiration Date: _____   Date of Birth: _____

| Type of Notarial Act: | ❑ Verbal Ceremony Performed | ❑ Other (Describe): | Fee: $ | |
| ❑ Oath/Affirmation | ❑ Acknowledgment | | Travel: $ | Right Thumbprint of Signer |

| Type of Document | Date of Document | Witness(es) Present ❑ Yes ❑ No | Other Signer(s) Present ❑ Yes ❑ No | |

| Witness: Printed Name | Address/Phone | Signature of Witness | |

| Comments; Additional Information: | If Notarization Failed or Refused, Give Reason: |
| | ❑ Insufficient ID   ❑ Signer Confused   ❑ Other (Explain in Comments Field) |

242

| Printed Name of Signer: | Signer's Signature: | Time AM/PM: _____ |
| | | Date Notarized: _____ |

| Signer's Complete Address: | City | State | Zip | Phone |

Identification by: ❑ Identification Card   Issued By: _____   I.D. # _____

❑ Personal Knowledge   ❑ Credible Witness(es)   Type of I.D.: _____   Expiration Date: _____   Date of Birth: _____

| Type of Notarial Act: | ❑ Verbal Ceremony Performed | ❑ Other (Describe): | Fee: $ | |
| ❑ Oath/Affirmation | ❑ Acknowledgment | | Travel: $ | Right Thumbprint of Signer |

| Type of Document | Date of Document | Witness(es) Present ❑ Yes ❑ No | Other Signer(s) Present ❑ Yes ❑ No | |

| Witness: Printed Name | Address/Phone | Signature of Witness | |

| Comments; Additional Information: | If Notarization Failed or Refused, Give Reason: |
| | ❑ Insufficient ID   ❑ Signer Confused   ❑ Other (Explain in Comments Field) |

243

| Printed Name of Signer: | Signer's Signature: | Time AM/PM: _____ |
| | | Date Notarized: _____ |

| Signer's Complete Address: | City | State | Zip | Phone |

Identification by: ❑ Identification Card   Issued By: _____   I.D. # _____

❑ Personal Knowledge   ❑ Credible Witness(es)   Type of I.D.: _____   Expiration Date: _____   Date of Birth: _____

| Type of Notarial Act: | ❑ Verbal Ceremony Performed | ❑ Other (Describe): | Fee: $ | |
| ❑ Oath/Affirmation | ❑ Acknowledgment | | Travel: $ | Right Thumbprint of Signer |

| Type of Document | Date of Document | Witness(es) Present ❑ Yes ❑ No | Other Signer(s) Present ❑ Yes ❑ No | |

| Witness: Printed Name | Address/Phone | Signature of Witness | |

| Comments; Additional Information: | If Notarization Failed or Refused, Give Reason: |
| | ❑ Insufficient ID   ❑ Signer Confused   ❑ Other (Explain in Comments Field) |

244

Printed Name of Signer:

Signer's Signature:

Time AM/PM: _____

Date Notarized: _____

Signer's Complete Address:　　City　　　　　　　　State　　Zip　　　　　Phone

Identification by:　　❑ Identification Card　　Issued By: _____　I.D. # _____

❑ Personal Knowledge　　❑ Credible Witness(es)　　Type of I.D.: _____　Expiration Date: _____　Date of Birth: _____

Type of Notarial Act:　　❑ Verbal Ceremony Performed　　❑ Other (Describe):　　　　　Fee: $

❑ Oath/Affirmation　　❑ Acknowledgment　　　　　　　　　　　　　　Travel: $

Right Thumbprint of Signer

Type of Document　　　　Date of Document　　Witness(es) Present　　Other Signer(s) Present

❑ Yes ❑ No　　❑ Yes ❑ No

Witness: Printed Name　　　　Address/Phone　　　　Signature of Witness

Comments; Additional Information:

If Notarization Failed or Refused, Give Reason:

❑ Insufficient ID　　❑ Signer Confused　　❑ Other (Explain in Comments Field)

245

Printed Name of Signer:

Signer's Signature:

Time AM/PM: _____

Date Notarized: _____

Signer's Complete Address:　　City　　　　　　　　State　　Zip　　　　　Phone

Identification by:　　❑ Identification Card　　Issued By: _____　I.D. # _____

❑ Personal Knowledge　　❑ Credible Witness(es)　　Type of I.D.: _____　Expiration Date: _____　Date of Birth: _____

Type of Notarial Act:　　❑ Verbal Ceremony Performed　　❑ Other (Describe):　　　　　Fee: $

❑ Oath/Affirmation　　❑ Acknowledgment　　　　　　　　　　　　　　Travel: $

Right Thumbprint of Signer

Type of Document　　　　Date of Document　　Witness(es) Present　　Other Signer(s) Present

❑ Yes ❑ No　　❑ Yes ❑ No

Witness: Printed Name　　　　Address/Phone　　　　Signature of Witness

Comments; Additional Information:

If Notarization Failed or Refused, Give Reason:

❑ Insufficient ID　　❑ Signer Confused　　❑ Other (Explain in Comments Field)

246

Printed Name of Signer:

Signer's Signature:

Time AM/PM: _____

Date Notarized: _____

Signer's Complete Address:　　City　　　　　　　　State　　Zip　　　　　Phone

Identification by:　　❑ Identification Card　　Issued By: _____　I.D. # _____

❑ Personal Knowledge　　❑ Credible Witness(es)　　Type of I.D.: _____　Expiration Date: _____　Date of Birth: _____

Type of Notarial Act:　　❑ Verbal Ceremony Performed　　❑ Other (Describe):　　　　　Fee: $

❑ Oath/Affirmation　　❑ Acknowledgment　　　　　　　　　　　　　　Travel: $

Right Thumbprint of Signer

Type of Document　　　　Date of Document　　Witness(es) Present　　Other Signer(s) Present

❑ Yes ❑ No　　❑ Yes ❑ No

Witness: Printed Name　　　　Address/Phone　　　　Signature of Witness

Comments; Additional Information:

If Notarization Failed or Refused, Give Reason:

❑ Insufficient ID　　❑ Signer Confused　　❑ Other (Explain in Comments Field)

247

| Printed Name of Signer: | Signer's Signature: | Time AM/PM: _____ |
| | | Date Notarized: _____ |

| Signer's Complete Address: | City | State | Zip | Phone |

| Identification by: | ❏ Identification Card | Issued By: _____ | I.D. # _____ |
| ❏ Personal Knowledge | ❏ Credible Witness(es) | Type of I.D.: _____ | Expiration Date: _____ | Date of Birth: _____ |

| Type of Notarial Act: | ❏ Verbal Ceremony Performed | ❏ Other (Describe): | Fee: $ |
| ❏ Oath/Affirmation | ❏ Acknowledgment | | Travel: $ |

| Type of Document | Date of Document | Witness(es) Present ❏ Yes ❏ No | Other Signer(s) Present ❏ Yes ❏ No |

| Witness: Printed Name | Address/Phone | Signature of Witness |

Right Thumbprint of Signer

| Comments; Additional Information: | If Notarization Failed or Refused, Give Reason: |
| | ❏ Insufficient ID   ❏ Signer Confused   ❏ Other (Explain in Comments Field) |

248

| Printed Name of Signer: | Signer's Signature: | Time AM/PM: _____ |
| | | Date Notarized: _____ |

| Signer's Complete Address: | City | State | Zip | Phone |

| Identification by: | ❏ Identification Card | Issued By: _____ | I.D. # _____ |
| ❏ Personal Knowledge | ❏ Credible Witness(es) | Type of I.D.: _____ | Expiration Date: _____ | Date of Birth: _____ |

| Type of Notarial Act: | ❏ Verbal Ceremony Performed | ❏ Other (Describe): | Fee: $ |
| ❏ Oath/Affirmation | ❏ Acknowledgment | | Travel: $ |

| Type of Document | Date of Document | Witness(es) Present ❏ Yes ❏ No | Other Signer(s) Present ❏ Yes ❏ No |

| Witness: Printed Name | Address/Phone | Signature of Witness |

Right Thumbprint of Signer

| Comments; Additional Information: | If Notarization Failed or Refused, Give Reason: |
| | ❏ Insufficient ID   ❏ Signer Confused   ❏ Other (Explain in Comments Field) |

249

| Printed Name of Signer: | Signer's Signature: | Time AM/PM: _____ |
| | | Date Notarized: _____ |

| Signer's Complete Address: | City | State | Zip | Phone |

| Identification by: | ❏ Identification Card | Issued By: _____ | I.D. # _____ |
| ❏ Personal Knowledge | ❏ Credible Witness(es) | Type of I.D.: _____ | Expiration Date: _____ | Date of Birth: _____ |

| Type of Notarial Act: | ❏ Verbal Ceremony Performed | ❏ Other (Describe): | Fee: $ |
| ❏ Oath/Affirmation | ❏ Acknowledgment | | Travel: $ |

| Type of Document | Date of Document | Witness(es) Present ❏ Yes ❏ No | Other Signer(s) Present ❏ Yes ❏ No |

| Witness: Printed Name | Address/Phone | Signature of Witness |

Right Thumbprint of Signer

| Comments; Additional Information: | If Notarization Failed or Refused, Give Reason: |
| | ❏ Insufficient ID   ❏ Signer Confused   ❏ Other (Explain in Comments Field) |

250

| Printed Name of Signer: | Signer's Signature: | Time AM/PM: _____ |
| | | Date Notarized: _____ |

Signer's Complete Address: City   State   Zip   Phone

Identification by: ❏ Identification Card   Issued By: _____   I.D. # _____

❏ Personal Knowledge   ❏ Credible Witness(es)   Type of I.D.: _____   Expiration Date: _____   Date of Birth: _____

Type of Notarial Act: ❏ Verbal Ceremony Performed   ❏ Other (Describe):   Fee: $

❏ Oath/Affirmation   ❏ Acknowledgment   Travel: $

Type of Document   Date of Document   Witness(es) Present   Other Signer(s) Present

     ❏ Yes ❏ No   ❏ Yes ❏ No

Witness: Printed Name   Address/Phone   Signature of Witness

Right Thumbprint of Signer

Comments; Additional Information: If Notarization Failed or Refused, Give Reason:

❏ Insufficient ID   ❏ Signer Confused   ❏ Other (Explain in Comments Field)

251

| Printed Name of Signer: | Signer's Signature: | Time AM/PM: _____ |
| | | Date Notarized: _____ |

Signer's Complete Address: City   State   Zip   Phone

Identification by: ❏ Identification Card   Issued By: _____   I.D. # _____

❏ Personal Knowledge   ❏ Credible Witness(es)   Type of I.D.: _____   Expiration Date: _____   Date of Birth: _____

Type of Notarial Act: ❏ Verbal Ceremony Performed   ❏ Other (Describe):   Fee: $

❏ Oath/Affirmation   ❏ Acknowledgment   Travel: $

Type of Document   Date of Document   Witness(es) Present   Other Signer(s) Present

     ❏ Yes ❏ No   ❏ Yes ❏ No

Witness: Printed Name   Address/Phone   Signature of Witness

Right Thumbprint of Signer

Comments; Additional Information: If Notarization Failed or Refused, Give Reason:

❏ Insufficient ID   ❏ Signer Confused   ❏ Other (Explain in Comments Field)

252

| Printed Name of Signer: | Signer's Signature: | Time AM/PM: _____ |
| | | Date Notarized: _____ |

Signer's Complete Address: City   State   Zip   Phone

Identification by: ❏ Identification Card   Issued By: _____   I.D. # _____

❏ Personal Knowledge   ❏ Credible Witness(es)   Type of I.D.: _____   Expiration Date: _____   Date of Birth: _____

Type of Notarial Act: ❏ Verbal Ceremony Performed   ❏ Other (Describe):   Fee: $

❏ Oath/Affirmation   ❏ Acknowledgment   Travel: $

Type of Document   Date of Document   Witness(es) Present   Other Signer(s) Present

     ❏ Yes ❏ No   ❏ Yes ❏ No

Witness: Printed Name   Address/Phone   Signature of Witness

Right Thumbprint of Signer

Comments; Additional Information: If Notarization Failed or Refused, Give Reason:

❏ Insufficient ID   ❏ Signer Confused   ❏ Other (Explain in Comments Field)

253

Printed Name of Signer:	Signer's Signature:	Time AM/PM: _____ Date Notarized: _____

Signer's Complete Address: City   State   Zip   Phone

Identification by: ❏ Identification Card   Issued By: _____   I.D. #_____

❏ Personal Knowledge   ❏ Credible Witness(es)   Type of I.D.:_____   Expiration Date: _____   Date of Birth: _____

Type of Notarial Act: ❏ Verbal Ceremony Performed   ❏ Other (Describe):   Fee: $ Travel: $

❏ Oath/Affirmation   ❏ Acknowledgment

Type of Document   Date of Document   Witness(es) Present   ❏ Yes ❏ No   Other Signer(s) Present   ❏ Yes ❏ No

Witness: Printed Name   Address/Phone   Signature of Witness

Right Thumbprint of Signer

Comments; Additional Information:

If Notarization Failed or Refused, Give Reason:
❏ Insufficient ID   ❏ Signer Confused   ❏ Other (Explain in Comments Field)

254

Printed Name of Signer:	Signer's Signature:	Time AM/PM: _____ Date Notarized: _____

Signer's Complete Address: City   State   Zip   Phone

Identification by: ❏ Identification Card   Issued By: _____   I.D. #_____

❏ Personal Knowledge   ❏ Credible Witness(es)   Type of I.D.:_____   Expiration Date: _____   Date of Birth: _____

Type of Notarial Act: ❏ Verbal Ceremony Performed   ❏ Other (Describe):   Fee: $ Travel: $

❏ Oath/Affirmation   ❏ Acknowledgment

Type of Document   Date of Document   Witness(es) Present   ❏ Yes ❏ No   Other Signer(s) Present   ❏ Yes ❏ No

Witness: Printed Name   Address/Phone   Signature of Witness

Right Thumbprint of Signer

Comments; Additional Information:

If Notarization Failed or Refused, Give Reason:
❏ Insufficient ID   ❏ Signer Confused   ❏ Other (Explain in Comments Field)

255

Printed Name of Signer:	Signer's Signature:	Time AM/PM: _____ Date Notarized: _____

Signer's Complete Address: City   State   Zip   Phone

Identification by: ❏ Identification Card   Issued By: _____   I.D. #_____

❏ Personal Knowledge   ❏ Credible Witness(es)   Type of I.D.:_____   Expiration Date: _____   Date of Birth: _____

Type of Notarial Act: ❏ Verbal Ceremony Performed   ❏ Other (Describe):   Fee: $ Travel: $

❏ Oath/Affirmation   ❏ Acknowledgment

Type of Document   Date of Document   Witness(es) Present   ❏ Yes ❏ No   Other Signer(s) Present   ❏ Yes ❏ No

Witness: Printed Name   Address/Phone   Signature of Witness

Right Thumbprint of Signer

Comments; Additional Information:

If Notarization Failed or Refused, Give Reason:
❏ Insufficient ID   ❏ Signer Confused   ❏ Other (Explain in Comments Field)

256

| Printed Name of Signer: | Signer's Signature: | Time AM/PM: _____ |
| | | Date Notarized: _____ |

| Signer's Complete Address: | City | State | Zip | Phone |

Identification by: ❑ Identification Card   Issued By: _____   I.D. # _____

❑ Personal Knowledge   ❑ Credible Witness(es)   Type of I.D.: _____   Expiration Date: _____   Date of Birth: _____

Type of Notarial Act: ❑ Verbal Ceremony Performed   ❑ Other (Describe):   Fee: $ _____

❑ Oath/Affirmation   ❑ Acknowledgment   Travel: $ _____

Type of Document   Date of Document   Witness(es) Present   ❑ Yes ❑ No   Other Signer(s) Present   ❑ Yes ❑ No

Right Thumbprint of Signer

Witness: Printed Name   Address/Phone   Signature of Witness

Comments; Additional Information:

If Notarization Failed or Refused, Give Reason:

❑ Insufficient ID   ❑ Signer Confused   ❑ Other (Explain in Comments Field)

257

| Printed Name of Signer: | Signer's Signature: | Time AM/PM: _____ |
| | | Date Notarized: _____ |

| Signer's Complete Address: | City | State | Zip | Phone |

Identification by: ❑ Identification Card   Issued By: _____   I.D. # _____

❑ Personal Knowledge   ❑ Credible Witness(es)   Type of I.D.: _____   Expiration Date: _____   Date of Birth: _____

Type of Notarial Act: ❑ Verbal Ceremony Performed   ❑ Other (Describe):   Fee: $ _____

❑ Oath/Affirmation   ❑ Acknowledgment   Travel: $ _____

Type of Document   Date of Document   Witness(es) Present   ❑ Yes ❑ No   Other Signer(s) Present   ❑ Yes ❑ No

Right Thumbprint of Signer

Witness: Printed Name   Address/Phone   Signature of Witness

Comments; Additional Information:

If Notarization Failed or Refused, Give Reason:

❑ Insufficient ID   ❑ Signer Confused   ❑ Other (Explain in Comments Field)

258

| Printed Name of Signer: | Signer's Signature: | Time AM/PM: _____ |
| | | Date Notarized: _____ |

| Signer's Complete Address: | City | State | Zip | Phone |

Identification by: ❑ Identification Card   Issued By: _____   I.D. # _____

❑ Personal Knowledge   ❑ Credible Witness(es)   Type of I.D.: _____   Expiration Date: _____   Date of Birth: _____

Type of Notarial Act: ❑ Verbal Ceremony Performed   ❑ Other (Describe):   Fee: $ _____

❑ Oath/Affirmation   ❑ Acknowledgment   Travel: $ _____

Type of Document   Date of Document   Witness(es) Present   ❑ Yes ❑ No   Other Signer(s) Present   ❑ Yes ❑ No

Right Thumbprint of Signer

Witness: Printed Name   Address/Phone   Signature of Witness

Comments; Additional Information:

If Notarization Failed or Refused, Give Reason:

❑ Insufficient ID   ❑ Signer Confused   ❑ Other (Explain in Comments Field)

259

| Printed Name of Signer: | Signer's Signature: | Time AM/PM: _____ |
| | | Date Notarized: _____ |

| Signer's Complete Address: | City | State | Zip | Phone |

| Identification by: | ❏ Identification Card | Issued By: _____ | I.D. # _____ |
| ❏ Personal Knowledge | ❏ Credible Witness(es) | Type of I.D.: _____ | Expiration Date: _____ | Date of Birth: _____ |

| Type of Notarial Act: | ❏ Verbal Ceremony Performed | ❏ Other (Describe): | Fee: $ | |
| ❏ Oath/Affirmation | ❏ Acknowledgment | | Travel: $ | |

| Type of Document | Date of Document | Witness(es) Present | Other Signer(s) Present | Right Thumbprint of Signer |
| | | ❏ Yes ❏ No | ❏ Yes ❏ No | |

| Witness: Printed Name | Address/Phone | Signature of Witness |

| Comments; Additional Information: | If Notarization Failed or Refused, Give Reason: |
| | ❏ Insufficient ID ❏ Signer Confused ❏ Other (Explain in Comments Field) |

260

| Printed Name of Signer: | Signer's Signature: | Time AM/PM: _____ |
| | | Date Notarized: _____ |

| Signer's Complete Address: | City | State | Zip | Phone |

| Identification by: | ❏ Identification Card | Issued By: _____ | I.D. # _____ |
| ❏ Personal Knowledge | ❏ Credible Witness(es) | Type of I.D.: _____ | Expiration Date: _____ | Date of Birth: _____ |

| Type of Notarial Act: | ❏ Verbal Ceremony Performed | ❏ Other (Describe): | Fee: $ | |
| ❏ Oath/Affirmation | ❏ Acknowledgment | | Travel: $ | |

| Type of Document | Date of Document | Witness(es) Present | Other Signer(s) Present | Right Thumbprint of Signer |
| | | ❏ Yes ❏ No | ❏ Yes ❏ No | |

| Witness: Printed Name | Address/Phone | Signature of Witness |

| Comments; Additional Information: | If Notarization Failed or Refused, Give Reason: |
| | ❏ Insufficient ID ❏ Signer Confused ❏ Other (Explain in Comments Field) |

261

| Printed Name of Signer: | Signer's Signature: | Time AM/PM: _____ |
| | | Date Notarized: _____ |

| Signer's Complete Address: | City | State | Zip | Phone |

| Identification by: | ❏ Identification Card | Issued By: _____ | I.D. # _____ |
| ❏ Personal Knowledge | ❏ Credible Witness(es) | Type of I.D.: _____ | Expiration Date: _____ | Date of Birth: _____ |

| Type of Notarial Act: | ❏ Verbal Ceremony Performed | ❏ Other (Describe): | Fee: $ | |
| ❏ Oath/Affirmation | ❏ Acknowledgment | | Travel: $ | |

| Type of Document | Date of Document | Witness(es) Present | Other Signer(s) Present | Right Thumbprint of Signer |
| | | ❏ Yes ❏ No | ❏ Yes ❏ No | |

| Witness: Printed Name | Address/Phone | Signature of Witness |

| Comments; Additional Information: | If Notarization Failed or Refused, Give Reason: |
| | ❏ Insufficient ID ❏ Signer Confused ❏ Other (Explain in Comments Field) |

262

Printed Name of Signer: | Signer's Signature: | Time AM/PM: _____
Date Notarized: _____

Signer's Complete Address: | City | State | Zip | Phone

Identification by: | ❏ Identification Card | Issued By: _____ | I.D. # _____

❏ Personal Knowledge | ❏ Credible Witness(es) | Type of I.D.: _____ | Expiration Date: _____ | Date of Birth: _____

Type of Notarial Act: | ❏ Verbal Ceremony Performed | ❏ Other (Describe): | Fee: $
❏ Oath/Affirmation | ❏ Acknowledgment | | Travel: $

Type of Document | Date of Document | Witness(es) Present | Other Signer(s) Present
| | ❏ Yes ❏ No | ❏ Yes ❏ No

Right Thumbprint of Signer

Witness: Printed Name | Address/Phone | Signature of Witness

Comments; Additional Information: | If Notarization Failed or Refused, Give Reason:
❏ Insufficient ID ❏ Signer Confused ❏ Other (Explain in Comments Field)

263

Printed Name of Signer: | Signer's Signature: | Time AM/PM: _____
Date Notarized: _____

Signer's Complete Address: | City | State | Zip | Phone

Identification by: | ❏ Identification Card | Issued By: _____ | I.D. # _____

❏ Personal Knowledge | ❏ Credible Witness(es) | Type of I.D.: _____ | Expiration Date: _____ | Date of Birth: _____

Type of Notarial Act: | ❏ Verbal Ceremony Performed | ❏ Other (Describe): | Fee: $
❏ Oath/Affirmation | ❏ Acknowledgment | | Travel: $

Type of Document | Date of Document | Witness(es) Present | Other Signer(s) Present
| | ❏ Yes ❏ No | ❏ Yes ❏ No

Right Thumbprint of Signer

Witness: Printed Name | Address/Phone | Signature of Witness

Comments; Additional Information: | If Notarization Failed or Refused, Give Reason:
❏ Insufficient ID ❏ Signer Confused ❏ Other (Explain in Comments Field)

264

Printed Name of Signer: | Signer's Signature: | Time AM/PM: _____
Date Notarized: _____

Signer's Complete Address: | City | State | Zip | Phone

Identification by: | ❏ Identification Card | Issued By: _____ | I.D. # _____

❏ Personal Knowledge | ❏ Credible Witness(es) | Type of I.D.: _____ | Expiration Date: _____ | Date of Birth: _____

Type of Notarial Act: | ❏ Verbal Ceremony Performed | ❏ Other (Describe): | Fee: $
❏ Oath/Affirmation | ❏ Acknowledgment | | Travel: $

Type of Document | Date of Document | Witness(es) Present | Other Signer(s) Present
| | ❏ Yes ❏ No | ❏ Yes ❏ No

Right Thumbprint of Signer

Witness: Printed Name | Address/Phone | Signature of Witness

Comments; Additional Information: | If Notarization Failed or Refused, Give Reason:
❏ Insufficient ID ❏ Signer Confused ❏ Other (Explain in Comments Field)

265

Printed Name of Signer:

Signer's Signature:

Time AM/PM: _____
Date Notarized: _____

Signer's Complete Address: City   State   Zip   Phone

Identification by: ❏ Identification Card   Issued By: _____   I.D. # _____

❏ Personal Knowledge   ❏ Credible Witness(es)   Type of I.D.: _____   Expiration Date: _____   Date of Birth: _____

Type of Notarial Act: ❏ Verbal Ceremony Performed   ❏ Other (Describe):   Fee: $
❏ Oath/Affirmation   ❏ Acknowledgment   Travel: $

Type of Document   Date of Document   Witness(es) Present   Other Signer(s) Present
                                                    ❏ Yes ❏ No   ❏ Yes ❏ No

Right Thumbprint of Signer

Witness: Printed Name   Address/Phone   Signature of Witness

Comments; Additional Information: If Notarization Failed or Refused, Give Reason:

                                             ❏ Insufficient ID   ❏ Signer Confused   ❏ Other (Explain in Comments Field)

266

Printed Name of Signer:

Signer's Signature:

Time AM/PM: _____
Date Notarized: _____

Signer's Complete Address: City   State   Zip   Phone

Identification by: ❏ Identification Card   Issued By: _____   I.D. # _____

❏ Personal Knowledge   ❏ Credible Witness(es)   Type of I.D.: _____   Expiration Date: _____   Date of Birth: _____

Type of Notarial Act: ❏ Verbal Ceremony Performed   ❏ Other (Describe):   Fee: $
❏ Oath/Affirmation   ❏ Acknowledgment   Travel: $

Type of Document   Date of Document   Witness(es) Present   Other Signer(s) Present
                                                    ❏ Yes ❏ No   ❏ Yes ❏ No

Right Thumbprint of Signer

Witness: Printed Name   Address/Phone   Signature of Witness

Comments; Additional Information: If Notarization Failed or Refused, Give Reason:

                                             ❏ Insufficient ID   ❏ Signer Confused   ❏ Other (Explain in Comments Field)

267

Printed Name of Signer:

Signer's Signature:

Time AM/PM: _____
Date Notarized: _____

Signer's Complete Address: City   State   Zip   Phone

Identification by: ❏ Identification Card   Issued By: _____   I.D. # _____

❏ Personal Knowledge   ❏ Credible Witness(es)   Type of I.D.: _____   Expiration Date: _____   Date of Birth: _____

Type of Notarial Act: ❏ Verbal Ceremony Performed   ❏ Other (Describe):   Fee: $
❏ Oath/Affirmation   ❏ Acknowledgment   Travel: $

Type of Document   Date of Document   Witness(es) Present   Other Signer(s) Present
                                                    ❏ Yes ❏ No   ❏ Yes ❏ No

Right Thumbprint of Signer

Witness: Printed Name   Address/Phone   Signature of Witness

Comments; Additional Information: If Notarization Failed or Refused, Give Reason:

                                             ❏ Insufficient ID   ❏ Signer Confused   ❏ Other (Explain in Comments Field)

268

Printed Name of Signer:

Signer's Signature:

Time AM/PM: _____

Date Notarized: _____

Signer's Complete Address: City   State   Zip   Phone

Identification by: ❑ Identification Card   Issued By: _____   I.D. # _____

❑ Personal Knowledge   ❑ Credible Witness(es)   Type of I.D.: _____   Expiration Date: _____   Date of Birth: _____

Type of Notarial Act: ❑ Verbal Ceremony Performed   ❑ Other (Describe):   Fee: $
❑ Oath/Affirmation   ❑ Acknowledgment   Travel: $

Type of Document   Date of Document   Witness(es) Present   Other Signer(s) Present
                                                ❑ Yes ❑ No   ❑ Yes ❑ No

Witness: Printed Name   Address/Phone   Signature of Witness

Right Thumbprint of Signer

Comments; Additional Information: If Notarization Failed or Refused, Give Reason:

❑ Insufficient ID   ❑ Signer Confused   ❑ Other (Explain in Comments Field)

269

Printed Name of Signer:

Signer's Signature:

Time AM/PM: _____

Date Notarized: _____

Signer's Complete Address: City   State   Zip   Phone

Identification by: ❑ Identification Card   Issued By: _____   I.D. # _____

❑ Personal Knowledge   ❑ Credible Witness(es)   Type of I.D.: _____   Expiration Date: _____   Date of Birth: _____

Type of Notarial Act: ❑ Verbal Ceremony Performed   ❑ Other (Describe):   Fee: $
❑ Oath/Affirmation   ❑ Acknowledgment   Travel: $

Type of Document   Date of Document   Witness(es) Present   Other Signer(s) Present
                                                ❑ Yes ❑ No   ❑ Yes ❑ No

Witness: Printed Name   Address/Phone   Signature of Witness

Right Thumbprint of Signer

Comments; Additional Information: If Notarization Failed or Refused, Give Reason:

❑ Insufficient ID   ❑ Signer Confused   ❑ Other (Explain in Comments Field)

270

Printed Name of Signer:

Signer's Signature:

Time AM/PM: _____

Date Notarized: _____

Signer's Complete Address: City   State   Zip   Phone

Identification by: ❑ Identification Card   Issued By: _____   I.D. # _____

❑ Personal Knowledge   ❑ Credible Witness(es)   Type of I.D.: _____   Expiration Date: _____   Date of Birth: _____

Type of Notarial Act: ❑ Verbal Ceremony Performed   ❑ Other (Describe):   Fee: $
❑ Oath/Affirmation   ❑ Acknowledgment   Travel: $

Type of Document   Date of Document   Witness(es) Present   Other Signer(s) Present
                                                ❑ Yes ❑ No   ❑ Yes ❑ No

Witness: Printed Name   Address/Phone   Signature of Witness

Right Thumbprint of Signer

Comments; Additional Information: If Notarization Failed or Refused, Give Reason:

❑ Insufficient ID   ❑ Signer Confused   ❑ Other (Explain in Comments Field)

271

Printed Name of Signer:

Signer's Signature:

Time AM/PM: _____

Date Notarized: _____

Signer's Complete Address: City   State   Zip   Phone

Identification by: ❏ Identification Card   Issued By: _____   I.D. # _____

❏ Personal Knowledge   ❏ Credible Witness(es)   Type of I.D.: _____   Expiration Date: _____   Date of Birth: _____

Type of Notarial Act: ❏ Verbal Ceremony Performed   ❏ Other (Describe):   Fee: $

❏ Oath/Affirmation   ❏ Acknowledgment   Travel: $

Type of Document   Date of Document   Witness(es) Present   Other Signer(s) Present

❏ Yes ❏ No   ❏ Yes ❏ No

Witness: Printed Name   Address/Phone   Signature of Witness

Right Thumbprint of Signer

Comments; Additional Information: If Notarization Failed or Refused, Give Reason:

❏ Insufficient ID   ❏ Signer Confused   ❏ Other (Explain in Comments Field)

272

Printed Name of Signer:

Signer's Signature:

Time AM/PM: _____

Date Notarized: _____

Signer's Complete Address: City   State   Zip   Phone

Identification by: ❏ Identification Card   Issued By: _____   I.D. # _____

❏ Personal Knowledge   ❏ Credible Witness(es)   Type of I.D.: _____   Expiration Date: _____   Date of Birth: _____

Type of Notarial Act: ❏ Verbal Ceremony Performed   ❏ Other (Describe):   Fee: $

❏ Oath/Affirmation   ❏ Acknowledgment   Travel: $

Type of Document   Date of Document   Witness(es) Present   Other Signer(s) Present

❏ Yes ❏ No   ❏ Yes ❏ No

Witness: Printed Name   Address/Phone   Signature of Witness

Right Thumbprint of Signer

Comments; Additional Information: If Notarization Failed or Refused, Give Reason:

❏ Insufficient ID   ❏ Signer Confused   ❏ Other (Explain in Comments Field)

273

Printed Name of Signer:

Signer's Signature:

Time AM/PM: _____

Date Notarized: _____

Signer's Complete Address: City   State   Zip   Phone

Identification by: ❏ Identification Card   Issued By: _____   I.D. # _____

❏ Personal Knowledge   ❏ Credible Witness(es)   Type of I.D.: _____   Expiration Date: _____   Date of Birth: _____

Type of Notarial Act: ❏ Verbal Ceremony Performed   ❏ Other (Describe):   Fee: $

❏ Oath/Affirmation   ❏ Acknowledgment   Travel: $

Type of Document   Date of Document   Witness(es) Present   Other Signer(s) Present

❏ Yes ❏ No   ❏ Yes ❏ No

Witness: Printed Name   Address/Phone   Signature of Witness

Right Thumbprint of Signer

Comments; Additional Information: If Notarization Failed or Refused, Give Reason:

❏ Insufficient ID   ❏ Signer Confused   ❏ Other (Explain in Comments Field)

Congratulations!

You have almost completed the entries in this notary journal. Don't risk losing your greatest protection against false claims or baseless lawsuits for rightfully performing your duties. Order your replacement journals today from NotaryTrainer.com. Save on shipping costs when you order 2 or more journals. While you are at the website, check out our new training products for notaries.

4 EASY WAYS TO REORDER: **CALL:** Toll Free 866-986-7446

INTERNET: www.notarytainer.com

Complete the order form at the front of this journal and send with payment to:

FAX: 732-553-0330 • 24-Hour Confidential Fax

MAIL: Notary Trainer/303 South Feltus St./South Amboy, NJ 08879

274

| Printed Name of Signer: | Signer's Signature: | Time AM/PM: _____ |
| | | Date Notarized: _____ |

Signer's Complete Address: City   State   Zip   Phone

Identification by: ❑ Identification Card   Issued By: _____   I.D. # _____

❑ Personal Knowledge   ❑ Credible Witness(es)   Type of I.D.: _____   Expiration Date: _____   Date of Birth: _____

Type of Notarial Act: ❑ Verbal Ceremony Performed   ❑ Other (Describe):   Fee: $

❑ Oath/Affirmation   ❑ Acknowledgment   Travel: $

Type of Document   Date of Document   Witness(es) Present   Other Signer(s) Present   Right Thumbprint of Signer

    ❑ Yes ❑ No   ❑ Yes ❑ No

Witness: Printed Name   Address/Phone   Signature of Witness

Comments; Additional Information: If Notarization Failed or Refused, Give Reason:

    ❑ Insufficient ID   ❑ Signer Confused   ❑ Other (Explain in Comments Field)

275

| Printed Name of Signer: | Signer's Signature: | Time AM/PM: _____ |
| | | Date Notarized: _____ |

Signer's Complete Address: City   State   Zip   Phone

Identification by: ❑ Identification Card   Issued By: _____   I.D. # _____

❑ Personal Knowledge   ❑ Credible Witness(es)   Type of I.D.: _____   Expiration Date: _____   Date of Birth: _____

Type of Notarial Act: ❑ Verbal Ceremony Performed   ❑ Other (Describe):   Fee: $

❑ Oath/Affirmation   ❑ Acknowledgment   Travel: $

Type of Document   Date of Document   Witness(es) Present   Other Signer(s) Present   Right Thumbprint of Signer

    ❑ Yes ❑ No   ❑ Yes ❑ No

Witness: Printed Name   Address/Phone   Signature of Witness

Comments; Additional Information: If Notarization Failed or Refused, Give Reason:

    ❑ Insufficient ID   ❑ Signer Confused   ❑ Other (Explain in Comments Field)

276

| Printed Name of Signer: | Signer's Signature: | Time AM/PM: _____ |
| | | Date Notarized: _____ |

| Signer's Complete Address: | City | State | Zip | Phone |

Identification by: ❑ Identification Card   Issued By: _____   I.D. # _____

❑ Personal Knowledge   ❑ Credible Witness(es)   Type of I.D.: _____   Expiration Date: _____   Date of Birth: _____

| Type of Notarial Act: | ❑ Verbal Ceremony Performed | ❑ Other (Describe): | Fee: $ | Right Thumbprint of Signer |
| ❑ Oath/Affirmation | ❑ Acknowledgment | | Travel: $ | |

| Type of Document | Date of Document | Witness(es) Present | Other Signer(s) Present |
| | | ❑ Yes ❑ No | ❑ Yes ❑ No |

| Witness: Printed Name | Address/Phone | Signature of Witness |

Comments; Additional Information:

If Notarization Failed or Refused, Give Reason:

❑ Insufficient ID   ❑ Signer Confused   ❑ Other (Explain in Comments Field)

277

| Printed Name of Signer: | Signer's Signature: | Time AM/PM: _____ |
| | | Date Notarized: _____ |

| Signer's Complete Address: | City | State | Zip | Phone |

Identification by: ❑ Identification Card   Issued By: _____   I.D. # _____

❑ Personal Knowledge   ❑ Credible Witness(es)   Type of I.D.: _____   Expiration Date: _____   Date of Birth: _____

| Type of Notarial Act: | ❑ Verbal Ceremony Performed | ❑ Other (Describe): | Fee: $ | Right Thumbprint of Signer |
| ❑ Oath/Affirmation | ❑ Acknowledgment | | Travel: $ | |

| Type of Document | Date of Document | Witness(es) Present | Other Signer(s) Present |
| | | ❑ Yes ❑ No | ❑ Yes ❑ No |

| Witness: Printed Name | Address/Phone | Signature of Witness |

Comments; Additional Information:

If Notarization Failed or Refused, Give Reason:

❑ Insufficient ID   ❑ Signer Confused   ❑ Other (Explain in Comments Field)

278

| Printed Name of Signer: | Signer's Signature: | Time AM/PM: _____ |
| | | Date Notarized: _____ |

| Signer's Complete Address: | City | State | Zip | Phone |

Identification by: ❑ Identification Card   Issued By: _____   I.D. # _____

❑ Personal Knowledge   ❑ Credible Witness(es)   Type of I.D.: _____   Expiration Date: _____   Date of Birth: _____

| Type of Notarial Act: | ❑ Verbal Ceremony Performed | ❑ Other (Describe): | Fee: $ | Right Thumbprint of Signer |
| ❑ Oath/Affirmation | ❑ Acknowledgment | | Travel: $ | |

| Type of Document | Date of Document | Witness(es) Present | Other Signer(s) Present |
| | | ❑ Yes ❑ No | ❑ Yes ❑ No |

| Witness: Printed Name | Address/Phone | Signature of Witness |

Comments; Additional Information:

If Notarization Failed or Refused, Give Reason:

❑ Insufficient ID   ❑ Signer Confused   ❑ Other (Explain in Comments Field)

279

Printed Name of Signer:	Signer's Signature:	Time AM/PM: _____
		Date Notarized: _____

Signer's Complete Address:	City	State	Zip	Phone

Identification by: ❑ Identification Card   Issued By: _____ I.D. # _____

❑ Personal Knowledge   ❑ Credible Witness(es)   Type of I.D.: _____   Expiration Date: _____   Date of Birth: _____

Type of Notarial Act: ❑ Verbal Ceremony Performed   ❑ Other (Describe):   Fee: $
❑ Oath/Affirmation   ❑ Acknowledgment   Travel: $

Type of Document	Date of Document	Witness(es) Present ❑ Yes ❑ No	Other Signer(s) Present ❑ Yes ❑ No	Right Thumbprint of Signer

Witness: Printed Name   Address/Phone   Signature of Witness

Comments; Additional Information: If Notarization Failed or Refused, Give Reason:

❑ Insufficient ID   ❑ Signer Confused   ❑ Other (Explain in Comments Field)

280

Printed Name of Signer:	Signer's Signature:	Time AM/PM: _____
		Date Notarized: _____

Signer's Complete Address:	City	State	Zip	Phone

Identification by: ❑ Identification Card   Issued By: _____ I.D. # _____

❑ Personal Knowledge   ❑ Credible Witness(es)   Type of I.D.: _____   Expiration Date: _____   Date of Birth: _____

Type of Notarial Act: ❑ Verbal Ceremony Performed   ❑ Other (Describe):   Fee: $
❑ Oath/Affirmation   ❑ Acknowledgment   Travel: $

Type of Document	Date of Document	Witness(es) Present ❑ Yes ❑ No	Other Signer(s) Present ❑ Yes ❑ No	Right Thumbprint of Signer

Witness: Printed Name   Address/Phone   Signature of Witness

Comments; Additional Information: If Notarization Failed or Refused, Give Reason:

❑ Insufficient ID   ❑ Signer Confused   ❑ Other (Explain in Comments Field)

281

Printed Name of Signer:	Signer's Signature:	Time AM/PM: _____
		Date Notarized: _____

Signer's Complete Address:	City	State	Zip	Phone

Identification by: ❑ Identification Card   Issued By: _____ I.D. # _____

❑ Personal Knowledge   ❑ Credible Witness(es)   Type of I.D.: _____   Expiration Date: _____   Date of Birth: _____

Type of Notarial Act: ❑ Verbal Ceremony Performed   ❑ Other (Describe):   Fee: $
❑ Oath/Affirmation   ❑ Acknowledgment   Travel: $

Type of Document	Date of Document	Witness(es) Present ❑ Yes ❑ No	Other Signer(s) Present ❑ Yes ❑ No	Right Thumbprint of Signer

Witness: Printed Name   Address/Phone   Signature of Witness

Comments; Additional Information: If Notarization Failed or Refused, Give Reason:

❑ Insufficient ID   ❑ Signer Confused   ❑ Other (Explain in Comments Field)

282

| Printed Name of Signer: | Signer's Signature: | Time AM/PM: _____ |
| | | Date Notarized: _____ |

Signer's Complete Address: City   State   Zip   Phone

Identification by: ❏ Identification Card   Issued By: _____   I.D. # _____

❏ Personal Knowledge   ❏ Credible Witness(es)   Type of I.D.: _____   Expiration Date: _____   Date of Birth: _____

Type of Notarial Act: ❏ Verbal Ceremony Performed   ❏ Other (Describe):   Fee: $

❏ Oath/Affirmation   ❏ Acknowledgment   Travel: $

Type of Document   Date of Document   Witness(es) Present   Other Signer(s) Present
                                         ❏ Yes ❏ No   ❏ Yes ❏ No

Right Thumbprint of Signer

Witness: Printed Name   Address/Phone   Signature of Witness

Comments; Additional Information: If Notarization Failed or Refused, Give Reason:

❏ Insufficient ID   ❏ Signer Confused   ❏ Other (Explain in Comments Field)

283

| Printed Name of Signer: | Signer's Signature: | Time AM/PM: _____ |
| | | Date Notarized: _____ |

Signer's Complete Address: City   State   Zip   Phone

Identification by: ❏ Identification Card   Issued By: _____   I.D. # _____

❏ Personal Knowledge   ❏ Credible Witness(es)   Type of I.D.: _____   Expiration Date: _____   Date of Birth: _____

Type of Notarial Act: ❏ Verbal Ceremony Performed   ❏ Other (Describe):   Fee: $

❏ Oath/Affirmation   ❏ Acknowledgment   Travel: $

Type of Document   Date of Document   Witness(es) Present   Other Signer(s) Present
                                         ❏ Yes ❏ No   ❏ Yes ❏ No

Right Thumbprint of Signer

Witness: Printed Name   Address/Phone   Signature of Witness

Comments; Additional Information: If Notarization Failed or Refused, Give Reason:

❏ Insufficient ID   ❏ Signer Confused   ❏ Other (Explain in Comments Field)

284

| Printed Name of Signer: | Signer's Signature: | Time AM/PM: _____ |
| | | Date Notarized: _____ |

Signer's Complete Address: City   State   Zip   Phone

Identification by: ❏ Identification Card   Issued By: _____   I.D. # _____

❏ Personal Knowledge   ❏ Credible Witness(es)   Type of I.D.: _____   Expiration Date: _____   Date of Birth: _____

Type of Notarial Act: ❏ Verbal Ceremony Performed   ❏ Other (Describe):   Fee: $

❏ Oath/Affirmation   ❏ Acknowledgment   Travel: $

Type of Document   Date of Document   Witness(es) Present   Other Signer(s) Present
                                         ❏ Yes ❏ No   ❏ Yes ❏ No

Right Thumbprint of Signer

Witness: Printed Name   Address/Phone   Signature of Witness

Comments; Additional Information: If Notarization Failed or Refused, Give Reason:

❏ Insufficient ID   ❏ Signer Confused   ❏ Other (Explain in Comments Field)

285

Printed Name of Signer: | Signer's Signature: | Time AM/PM: _____
Date Notarized: _____

Signer's Complete Address: | City | State | Zip | Phone

Identification by: ❑ Identification Card | Issued By: _____ | I.D. # _____

❑ Personal Knowledge ❑ Credible Witness(es) | Type of I.D.: _____ | Expiration Date: _____ | Date of Birth: _____

Type of Notarial Act: ❑ Verbal Ceremony Performed | ❑ Other (Describe): | Fee: $
❑ Oath/Affirmation ❑ Acknowledgment | | Travel: $

Type of Document | Date of Document | Witness(es) Present ❑ Yes ❑ No | Other Signer(s) Present ❑ Yes ❑ No

Right Thumbprint of Signer

Witness: Printed Name | Address/Phone | Signature of Witness

Comments; Additional Information: | If Notarization Failed or Refused, Give Reason:
❑ Insufficient ID ❑ Signer Confused ❑ Other (Explain in Comments Field)

286

Printed Name of Signer: | Signer's Signature: | Time AM/PM: _____
Date Notarized: _____

Signer's Complete Address: | City | State | Zip | Phone

Identification by: ❑ Identification Card | Issued By: _____ | I.D. # _____

❑ Personal Knowledge ❑ Credible Witness(es) | Type of I.D.: _____ | Expiration Date: _____ | Date of Birth: _____

Type of Notarial Act: ❑ Verbal Ceremony Performed | ❑ Other (Describe): | Fee: $
❑ Oath/Affirmation ❑ Acknowledgment | | Travel: $

Type of Document | Date of Document | Witness(es) Present ❑ Yes ❑ No | Other Signer(s) Present ❑ Yes ❑ No

Right Thumbprint of Signer

Witness: Printed Name | Address/Phone | Signature of Witness

Comments; Additional Information: | If Notarization Failed or Refused, Give Reason:
❑ Insufficient ID ❑ Signer Confused ❑ Other (Explain in Comments Field)

287

Printed Name of Signer: | Signer's Signature: | Time AM/PM: _____
Date Notarized: _____

Signer's Complete Address: | City | State | Zip | Phone

Identification by: ❑ Identification Card | Issued By: _____ | I.D. # _____

❑ Personal Knowledge ❑ Credible Witness(es) | Type of I.D.: _____ | Expiration Date: _____ | Date of Birth: _____

Type of Notarial Act: ❑ Verbal Ceremony Performed | ❑ Other (Describe): | Fee: $
❑ Oath/Affirmation ❑ Acknowledgment | | Travel: $

Type of Document | Date of Document | Witness(es) Present ❑ Yes ❑ No | Other Signer(s) Present ❑ Yes ❑ No

Right Thumbprint of Signer

Witness: Printed Name | Address/Phone | Signature of Witness

Comments; Additional Information: | If Notarization Failed or Refused, Give Reason:
❑ Insufficient ID ❑ Signer Confused ❑ Other (Explain in Comments Field)

288

| Printed Name of Signer: | Signer's Signature: | Time AM/PM: _____ |
| | | Date Notarized: _____ |

| Signer's Complete Address: | City | State | Zip | Phone |

| Identification by: | ❑ Identification Card | Issued By: _____ | I.D. # _____ |
| ❑ Personal Knowledge | ❑ Credible Witness(es) | Type of I.D.: _____ | Expiration Date: _____ | Date of Birth: _____ |

| Type of Notarial Act: | ❑ Verbal Ceremony Performed | ❑ Other (Describe): | Fee: $ | |
| ❑ Oath/Affirmation | ❑ Acknowledgment | | Travel: $ | Right Thumbprint of Signer |

| Type of Document | Date of Document | Witness(es) Present | Other Signer(s) Present | |
| | | ❑ Yes ❑ No | ❑ Yes ❑ No | |

| Witness: Printed Name | Address/Phone | Signature of Witness | |

| Comments; Additional Information: | If Notarization Failed or Refused, Give Reason: |
| | ❑ Insufficient ID   ❑ Signer Confused   ❑ Other (Explain in Comments Field) |

289

| Printed Name of Signer: | Signer's Signature: | Time AM/PM: _____ |
| | | Date Notarized: _____ |

| Signer's Complete Address: | City | State | Zip | Phone |

| Identification by: | ❑ Identification Card | Issued By: _____ | I.D. # _____ |
| ❑ Personal Knowledge | ❑ Credible Witness(es) | Type of I.D.: _____ | Expiration Date: _____ | Date of Birth: _____ |

| Type of Notarial Act: | ❑ Verbal Ceremony Performed | ❑ Other (Describe): | Fee: $ | |
| ❑ Oath/Affirmation | ❑ Acknowledgment | | Travel: $ | Right Thumbprint of Signer |

| Type of Document | Date of Document | Witness(es) Present | Other Signer(s) Present | |
| | | ❑ Yes ❑ No | ❑ Yes ❑ No | |

| Witness: Printed Name | Address/Phone | Signature of Witness | |

| Comments; Additional Information: | If Notarization Failed or Refused, Give Reason: |
| | ❑ Insufficient ID   ❑ Signer Confused   ❑ Other (Explain in Comments Field) |

290

| Printed Name of Signer: | Signer's Signature: | Time AM/PM: _____ |
| | | Date Notarized: _____ |

| Signer's Complete Address: | City | State | Zip | Phone |

| Identification by: | ❑ Identification Card | Issued By: _____ | I.D. # _____ |
| ❑ Personal Knowledge | ❑ Credible Witness(es) | Type of I.D.: _____ | Expiration Date: _____ | Date of Birth: _____ |

| Type of Notarial Act: | ❑ Verbal Ceremony Performed | ❑ Other (Describe): | Fee: $ | |
| ❑ Oath/Affirmation | ❑ Acknowledgment | | Travel: $ | Right Thumbprint of Signer |

| Type of Document | Date of Document | Witness(es) Present | Other Signer(s) Present | |
| | | ❑ Yes ❑ No | ❑ Yes ❑ No | |

| Witness: Printed Name | Address/Phone | Signature of Witness | |

| Comments; Additional Information: | If Notarization Failed or Refused, Give Reason: |
| | ❑ Insufficient ID   ❑ Signer Confused   ❑ Other (Explain in Comments Field) |

291

Printed Name of Signer:

Signer's Signature:

Time AM/PM: _____

Date Notarized: _____

Signer's Complete Address: City   State   Zip   Phone

Identification by: ❏ Identification Card   Issued By: _____   I.D. #_____

❏ Personal Knowledge   ❏ Credible Witness(es)   Type of I.D.:_____   Expiration Date: _____   Date of Birth: _____

Type of Notarial Act: ❏ Verbal Ceremony Performed   ❏ Other (Describe):   Fee: $

❏ Oath/Affirmation   ❏ Acknowledgment   Travel: $

Type of Document   Date of Document   Witness(es) Present   Other Signer(s) Present

   ❏ Yes ❏ No   ❏ Yes ❏ No

Witness: Printed Name   Address/Phone   Signature of Witness

Right Thumbprint of Signer

Comments; Additional Information:

If Notarization Failed or Refused, Give Reason:

❏ Insufficient ID   ❏ Signer Confused   ❏ Other (Explain in Comments Field)

292

Printed Name of Signer:

Signer's Signature:

Time AM/PM: _____

Date Notarized: _____

Signer's Complete Address: City   State   Zip   Phone

Identification by: ❏ Identification Card   Issued By: _____   I.D. #_____

❏ Personal Knowledge   ❏ Credible Witness(es)   Type of I.D.:_____   Expiration Date: _____   Date of Birth: _____

Type of Notarial Act: ❏ Verbal Ceremony Performed   ❏ Other (Describe):   Fee: $

❏ Oath/Affirmation   ❏ Acknowledgment   Travel: $

Type of Document   Date of Document   Witness(es) Present   Other Signer(s) Present

   ❏ Yes ❏ No   ❏ Yes ❏ No

Witness: Printed Name   Address/Phone   Signature of Witness

Right Thumbprint of Signer

Comments; Additional Information:

If Notarization Failed or Refused, Give Reason:

❏ Insufficient ID   ❏ Signer Confused   ❏ Other (Explain in Comments Field)

293

Printed Name of Signer:

Signer's Signature:

Time AM/PM: _____

Date Notarized: _____

Signer's Complete Address: City   State   Zip   Phone

Identification by: ❏ Identification Card   Issued By: _____   I.D. #_____

❏ Personal Knowledge   ❏ Credible Witness(es)   Type of I.D.:_____   Expiration Date: _____   Date of Birth: _____

Type of Notarial Act: ❏ Verbal Ceremony Performed   ❏ Other (Describe):   Fee: $

❏ Oath/Affirmation   ❏ Acknowledgment   Travel: $

Type of Document   Date of Document   Witness(es) Present   Other Signer(s) Present

   ❏ Yes ❏ No   ❏ Yes ❏ No

Witness: Printed Name   Address/Phone   Signature of Witness

Right Thumbprint of Signer

Comments; Additional Information:

If Notarization Failed or Refused, Give Reason:

❏ Insufficient ID   ❏ Signer Confused   ❏ Other (Explain in Comments Field)

294

| Printed Name of Signer: | Signer's Signature: | Time AM/PM: _____ |
| | | Date Notarized: _____ |

| Signer's Complete Address: | City | State | Zip | Phone |

| Identification by: | ☐ Identification Card | Issued By: _____ | I.D. # _____ |

| ☐ Personal Knowledge | ☐ Credible Witness(es) | Type of I.D.: _____ | Expiration Date: _____ | Date of Birth: _____ |

| Type of Notarial Act: | ☐ Verbal Ceremony Performed | ☐ Other (Describe): | Fee: $ | Right Thumbprint of Signer |
| ☐ Oath/Affirmation | ☐ Acknowledgment | | Travel: $ | |

| Type of Document | Date of Document | Witness(es) Present ☐ Yes ☐ No | Other Signer(s) Present ☐ Yes ☐ No | |

| Witness: Printed Name | Address/Phone | Signature of Witness | |

| Comments; Additional Information: | If Notarization Failed or Refused, Give Reason: |
| | ☐ Insufficient ID ☐ Signer Confused ☐ Other (Explain in Comments Field) |

295

| Printed Name of Signer: | Signer's Signature: | Time AM/PM: _____ |
| | | Date Notarized: _____ |

| Signer's Complete Address: | City | State | Zip | Phone |

| Identification by: | ☐ Identification Card | Issued By: _____ | I.D. # _____ |

| ☐ Personal Knowledge | ☐ Credible Witness(es) | Type of I.D.: _____ | Expiration Date: _____ | Date of Birth: _____ |

| Type of Notarial Act: | ☐ Verbal Ceremony Performed | ☐ Other (Describe): | Fee: $ | Right Thumbprint of Signer |
| ☐ Oath/Affirmation | ☐ Acknowledgment | | Travel: $ | |

| Type of Document | Date of Document | Witness(es) Present ☐ Yes ☐ No | Other Signer(s) Present ☐ Yes ☐ No | |

| Witness: Printed Name | Address/Phone | Signature of Witness | |

| Comments; Additional Information: | If Notarization Failed or Refused, Give Reason: |
| | ☐ Insufficient ID ☐ Signer Confused ☐ Other (Explain in Comments Field) |

296

| Printed Name of Signer: | Signer's Signature: | Time AM/PM: _____ |
| | | Date Notarized: _____ |

| Signer's Complete Address: | City | State | Zip | Phone |

| Identification by: | ☐ Identification Card | Issued By: _____ | I.D. # _____ |

| ☐ Personal Knowledge | ☐ Credible Witness(es) | Type of I.D.: _____ | Expiration Date: _____ | Date of Birth: _____ |

| Type of Notarial Act: | ☐ Verbal Ceremony Performed | ☐ Other (Describe): | Fee: $ | Right Thumbprint of Signer |
| ☐ Oath/Affirmation | ☐ Acknowledgment | | Travel: $ | |

| Type of Document | Date of Document | Witness(es) Present ☐ Yes ☐ No | Other Signer(s) Present ☐ Yes ☐ No | |

| Witness: Printed Name | Address/Phone | Signature of Witness | |

| Comments; Additional Information: | If Notarization Failed or Refused, Give Reason: |
| | ☐ Insufficient ID ☐ Signer Confused ☐ Other (Explain in Comments Field) |

297

Printed Name of Signer:

Signer's Signature:

Time AM/PM: _____

Date Notarized: _____

Signer's Complete Address: City   State   Zip   Phone

Identification by: ❏ Identification Card   Issued By: _____   I.D. # _____

❏ Personal Knowledge   ❏ Credible Witness(es)   Type of I.D.: _____   Expiration Date: _____   Date of Birth: _____

Type of Notarial Act: ❏ Verbal Ceremony Performed   ❏ Other (Describe):   Fee: $

❏ Oath/Affirmation   ❏ Acknowledgment   Travel: $

Type of Document   Date of Document   Witness(es) Present   Other Signer(s) Present   Right Thumbprint of Signer

❏ Yes ❏ No   ❏ Yes ❏ No

Witness: Printed Name   Address/Phone   Signature of Witness

Comments; Additional Information: If Notarization Failed or Refused, Give Reason:

❏ Insufficient ID   ❏ Signer Confused   ❏ Other (Explain in Comments Field)

298

Printed Name of Signer:

Signer's Signature:

Time AM/PM: _____

Date Notarized: _____

Signer's Complete Address: City   State   Zip   Phone

Identification by: ❏ Identification Card   Issued By: _____   I.D. # _____

❏ Personal Knowledge   ❏ Credible Witness(es)   Type of I.D.: _____   Expiration Date: _____   Date of Birth: _____

Type of Notarial Act: ❏ Verbal Ceremony Performed   ❏ Other (Describe):   Fee: $

❏ Oath/Affirmation   ❏ Acknowledgment   Travel: $

Type of Document   Date of Document   Witness(es) Present   Other Signer(s) Present   Right Thumbprint of Signer

❏ Yes ❏ No   ❏ Yes ❏ No

Witness: Printed Name   Address/Phone   Signature of Witness

Comments; Additional Information: If Notarization Failed or Refused, Give Reason:

❏ Insufficient ID   ❏ Signer Confused   ❏ Other (Explain in Comments Field)

299

Printed Name of Signer:

Signer's Signature:

Time AM/PM: _____

Date Notarized: _____

Signer's Complete Address: City   State   Zip   Phone

Identification by: ❏ Identification Card   Issued By: _____   I.D. # _____

❏ Personal Knowledge   ❏ Credible Witness(es)   Type of I.D.: _____   Expiration Date: _____   Date of Birth: _____

Type of Notarial Act: ❏ Verbal Ceremony Performed   ❏ Other (Describe):   Fee: $

❏ Oath/Affirmation   ❏ Acknowledgment   Travel: $

Type of Document   Date of Document   Witness(es) Present   Other Signer(s) Present   Right Thumbprint of Signer

❏ Yes ❏ No   ❏ Yes ❏ No

Witness: Printed Name   Address/Phone   Signature of Witness

Comments; Additional Information: If Notarization Failed or Refused, Give Reason:

❏ Insufficient ID   ❏ Signer Confused   ❏ Other (Explain in Comments Field)